'Our understanding of mental health has long been waiting for some fundamental rethinking. This book sets out a new framework that achieves the rare combination of being both revolutionary and eminently sensible. People have been complaining of "the medical model" for years but have rarely had anything to replace it with. Now we have an approach carefully worked out over several years by a group of senior psychologists and users of psychiatric services. "Chemical imbalances" have been replaced by a deeply social and experiential view. As the arguments about it go back and forth over the coming years, this book will be essential reading for anyone who takes a serious interest in the field.'
Richard Wilkinson, Emeritus Professor of Social Epidemiology, University of Nottingham, and co-author of *The Spirit Level* and *The Inner Level*

'We found the book to be self-explanatory, gripping and with good flow. The way in which it unravels is engaging and each paragraph leaves you wanting to know more. The added dimension of examples throughout makes this book relatable and also further supports learning. We believe that this book leaves people with no option but to think about change, not only within themselves, which in itself is empowering, but also within different cultures and the system as a whole. The knowledge it shares left us feeling empowered and we strongly believe it holds potential to have the same impact on others.'
SHIFT recovery community, Portsmouth

'This is a welcome and much needed contribution to current thinking in mental health. I couldn't put it down and will continue returning to it repeatedly. It is thoughtful, thought-provoking, engaging and refreshing. The Power Threat Meaning Framework has been a game-changer for many and this book synthesises it into everyday, jargon-free language, not only making it more accessible to a wider audience but also bringing the concepts alive and allowing the reader to apply it to their own experiences and/or to their practice. It offers an alternative to diagnosis and medical explanations and invites the reader to consider and reflect on other possibilities and avenues to make sense of emotional distress. There are also incredibly useful references to literature and research throughout, as well as real-life examples and powerful vignettes.'

Dr Karen Treisman MBE, clinical psychologist, organisational consultant, trainer, director of Safe Hands and Thinking Minds, and author of 11 books, including A Therapeutic Treasure Box for Working with Developmental Trauma

'This is a ground-breaking text on the impact of painful life experiences and trauma. It makes a huge contribution to the study of the human condition per se. The authors powerfully evidence their argument that emotional distress and the troubling behaviour and mental states that often ensue should no longer be seen as stigmatising mental illnesses, but rather as a part of life. The Power Threat Meaning Framework is a non-medical model of human distress (people with problems not patients with illnesses) offering real hope through collaborative conversations and narratives, and the consideration of social contexts, the influence of power and the meanings the person has taken from their experiences. Beautifully articulated and totally accessible to professionals and lay people alike, the book presents a radical shift from the expert narratives of the psychiatric model. This is a persuasive and commanding exhortation to review our fundamental assumptions and attitudes about mental health.'

Dr Margot Sunderland, Director of Education and Training at the Centre for Child Mental Health, London and Co-Director of Trauma-Informed Schools UK

THE POWER THREAT MEANING FRAMEWORK

AN ALTERNATIVE TO PSYCHIATRIC DIAGNOSIS

MARY BOYLE & LUCY JOHNSTONE

PCCS BOOKS

Published 2020

PCCS Books Ltd
Wyastone Business Park
Wyastone Leys
Monmouth
NP25 3SR
UK

Tel +44 (0)1600 891509
contact@pccs-books.co.uk
www.pccs-books.co.uk

*A Straight Talking Introduction to the Power Threat Meaning Framework:
An alternative to psychiatric diagnosis*

British Library Cataloguing in Publication Data.
A catalogue record for this book is available from the British Library

ISBNs
paperback – 978 1 910919 71 2
epub – 978 1 910919 72 9

Cover design by Jason Anscomb
Printed in the UK by ImprintDigital, Exeter

A Straight Talking Introduction to the Power Threat Meaning Framework: An alternative to psychiatric diagnosis

Contents

Author biographies

Mary Boyle has worked mainly in clinical psychology education and training and in clinical posts in adult mental health and women's health. She is a long-time critic of the medical/diagnostic approach and of individualistic approaches more generally in the health field. She is the author of *Schizophrenia: A scientific delusion* (2002) and *Rethinking Abortion: Psychology, gender, power and the law* (1997), as well as many articles and chapters on feminist approaches to women's health and on problems of and alternatives to diagnostic models. She is Emeritus Professor of Clinical Psychology at the University of East London.

Lucy Johnstone is a clinical psychologist. Her interest in critiques of and alternatives to current models of distress stems from her many years of working in adult mental health services, alternating with academic posts. She is the author of several books – *Users and Abusers of Psychiatry* (2000); *Formulation in Psychology and Psychotherapy* (2013) and *A Straight Talking Introduction to Psychiatric Diagnosis* (2014), and a number of chapters and articles taking a critical perspective on psychiatric theory and practice. She now works as an independent trainer.

Acknowledgements

We would like to thank the rest of the PTMF team – John Cromby, Jacqui Dillon, Dave Harper, Peter Kinderman, Eleanor Longden, Dave Pilgrim, John Read, and research assistant Kate Allsopp – for all their hard work over the five-year period of the project, and for their ongoing support in disseminating the ideas.

We are very grateful to the SHIFT Recovery Community for taking time to read and give feedback on the manuscript in preparation.

We also thank Catherine Jackson for her meticulous and supportive editing, and PCCS Books for helping us take the PTMF to new audiences.

Introducing the
Straight Talking Introductions
series

What are mental health problems?

Much of what is written and spoken about emotional distress or mental health problems implies that they are illnesses. This can lead us all too easily to believe that we no longer have to think about mental health problems, because illness is best left to doctors. They are the illness experts, and psychiatrists are the doctors who specialise in mental illness. This series of books is different because we don't think that all mental health problems should be automatically regarded as illnesses.

If mental health problems aren't necessarily illnesses, it means that the burden of responsibility for distress in our lives should not be entirely shouldered by doctors and psychiatrists. All citizens have a responsibility, however small, in creating a world where everyone has a decent opportunity to live a fulfilling life. This is a contentious idea, but one that we want to advance, alongside the dominant medical view.

Rather than accept that the ways of understanding and solutions to mental health problems are 'owned' by the medical profession, we will take a good look at alternatives that involve the users of psychiatric services, their carers, families, friends and other 'ordinary people' taking control of their own lives, and that means all of us. One of the tools required in order to become active in mental health issues, whether your own or other people's, is knowledge. This series of books is a starting point for anyone who wants to know more about mental health.

How these books are written

Information

We want these books to be understandable, so we use everyday language wherever possible. The books could have been almost completely jargon-free, but we thought that including some technical and medical terms would be helpful. Most doctors, psychiatrists and psychologists use the medical model of mental illness and manuals to help them diagnose mental health problems. The medical model and the diagnostic manuals use a particular set of terms to describe what doctors think of as 'conditions'. Although these words aren't very good at describing individual people's experiences, they are used a lot in psychiatric and psychological services, so we thought it would be helpful to define these terms as we went along and use them in a way that might help readers understand what the professionals mean. We don't expect that psychiatrists and psychologists and others working in mental health services will stop using medical terminology (although we think it would be respectful for them to drop them when talking to their patients and their families), so these books should help you get used to and learn *their* language.

The books also contain resources for further learning. As well as lists of books, websites and organisations at the end of the book, there are references. These will not be important to everyone, but they do tell the reader where information – a claim about effectiveness, an argument for or against, or a quotation – has come from, so you can follow it up if you wish.

Being realistic and reassuring

Our aim is to be realistic – neither overly optimistic nor pessimistic. Things are nearly always more complicated than we would like them to be. Honest evaluations of mental health problems, of what might cause them, of what can help, and of what the likely outcome might be, are, like so much in life, somewhere in between. For the vast majority of people, it would be wrong to say that they have an illness from which they will never recover. But it would be equally wrong to say that they will be completely unchanged by the distressing thoughts and feelings they are having. Life is an accumulation of experiences. There is almost certainly no pill, or any other treatment for that matter, that will take us back to 'how we were before'. There are many things we can do (and we look at lots of them in this series), in collaboration with doctors, psychiatrists, psychologists and counsellors, and, indeed, everyone working in mental health services; with the help of our friends and family, or on our own, that stand a good chance of helping us feel better and build a constructive life, with hope for the future.

Of course, we understand that the experiences dealt with in these books can sometimes be so overwhelming, confusing and terrifying that people will try to escape from them by withdrawing, going mad or even trying to kill themselves. This happens when our usual coping strategies fail us. We accept that killing oneself is, in some circumstances, a rational act – that, for the person in question, it can make a lot of sense. Nonetheless, we believe that much of the distress that underpins such an extreme course of action, from which there can be no turning back, is avoidable. For this reason, all of the books in this series point towards realistic hope and recovery.

Debates

There is no single convenient answer to many of the most important questions explored in these books. No matter how badly we might wish for a simple answer, what we have is a series of debates, or arguments, more like, between stakeholders, and there are many stakeholders whose voices demand space in these books. We use the word 'stakeholders' here because service users, carers, friends, family, doctors, psychologists, psychiatrists, nurses and other healthcare workers, scientists in drug companies, therapists, indeed all citizens, have a stake in how our society understands and deals with problems of mental health. It is simultaneously big business and intimately personal, and many things in between. As we go along, we try to explain how someone's stake in distress (including our own, where we can see it), whether professional or personal, can influence their experience and judgement.

While we want to present competing (sometimes opposing) viewpoints, we don't want to leave the reader high and dry to evaluate complicated debates on their own. We will try to present reasonable conclusions that might point in certain directions for personal action. Above all, though, we believe that knowledge is power and that the better informed you are, even though the information might be conflicting, the more able you will be to make sound decisions.

It's also useful to be reminded that the professionals involved in helping distressed people are themselves caught in the same flow of conflicting information. It is their *job*, however, to interpret it in our service, so that the best solutions are available to as many people as possible. You may have noticed that the word 'best' brings with it certain challenges, not least defining what we mean when we use this term. Perhaps 'the best' means the most effective? However, even using words like 'effective' doesn't completely clear up the puzzle. An effective treatment for an employer could be the one that returns a member of staff to work quickly; for a parent, it could be one that makes their child feel happier and calmer. For the government or the NHS, or someone running a private healthcare business, 'effective' might mean 'cost-effective'. This brings us to evidence.

Evidence

Throughout these books there will be material that we will present as 'evidence'. This is one of the most contentious terms to be found in this series. One person's evidence is another person's fanciful mythology and yet another person's oppressive propaganda. Nevertheless, the term crops up increasingly in everyday settings, most relevantly when we hear of 'evidence-based practice'. The idea behind this term is that the treatments psychologists and psychiatrists offer should be those that 'work'. Crudely put, there should be some evidence that, say, talking about problems or taking a prescribed drug actually helps people feel better. We encounter a real problem, however, when trying to evaluate this evidence, as the books in this series will demonstrate. We will try not to discount any 'evidence' out of hand, but we will critically evaluate it, and we will do this with a bias towards scientific evaluation.

The types of evidence that will be covered in these books, along with their positive and negative points, include the following.

Research methods, numbers and statistics

On the one hand, the logic of most research is simple, but on the other hand, the way things have to be arranged to avoid bias in the results can lead to a perplexing system of measurements. Even the experts lose the sense of it, sometimes. We'll try to explain the logic of studies, but almost certainly leave out the details. You can look these up yourself if you wish.

The books in this series look at research into a wide range of issues relating to mental health problems, including the experience of distress, what is known about the causes of problems and their prevention and treatment. Different research methods are appropriate for each of these areas, so we will be looking at different types of research as we go along. We say this now because many readers may be most familiar with studies into the *effective treatments* of distress, and we want to emphasise that there are many other credible and valid sources of essential information about distress that are sometimes overlooked.

You may have come across the idea that some research methods are 'better' than others – that they constitute a 'gold standard'. In the case of research into the effectiveness of different treatments, the gold standard is usually considered to be 'randomised controlled trials' (RCTs). In simple terms, RCTs are complex (and often very expensive) experiments in which a group of individuals who all suffer from the same problem are allocated randomly to a treatment (such as a drug or a form of talking therapy) or a 'control' treatment (at its simplest, no treatment at all, or a dummy pill or 'placebo') to test if the treatment works. We are not necessarily convinced that RCTs always *are* the best way of proving the effectiveness of different treatments, but they are, currently, the method given most credence by the bodies that control funding and what it is spent on, such as (in England) the National Institute for Health and Care Excellence (NICE) – so we need to understand them.

Before it is accepted by academics and clinicians, research must be written up and published in a journal that employs independent people to read it, to make sure that it is *bona fide* and that no glaring mistakes have been made. In recent years, a number of high-profile academics and scientific commentators have drawn attention to possible problems with this system of quality control. This series of books is not the place to deal with these arguments, but where they impinge on the evidence in a particular area, we will make sure it is highlighted.

Personal experience

Personal experience is an important source of evidence, to the extent that, nowadays, people who have suffered debilitating psychiatric distress are sometimes called 'experts by experience'. Personal stories provide an essential counterbalance to the impersonal numbers and statistics often found in research projects such as RCTs. While not everyone is average, by definition, most people are. Balancing the average results obtained from RCTs with some personal stories helps complete the picture and is now widely accepted, to the extent that it has given birth to the new field of 'survivor research'.

Understanding contexts

Widening our view to include people's families and lives and the cultural, economic, social and political settings in which we live completes the picture. Mental health problems are connected to the conditions in which we all live, just as much as they are connected to our biology. From the start, we want readers to know that, if there is one message or model that these books are trying to get across, it is that problems in mental health are more often than not the result of complex events in the environments in which we live and our reactions to them. These reactions can be also be influenced by our biology and the way we have learned to think and feel. Hopefully, these books will help disentangle the puzzle of distress and provide positive suggestions and hope for us all, whether we work in the system, currently have mental health problems ourselves or are caring for someone or friends with someone who has.

We hope that readers of these books will feel empowered by what they learn and thereby feel more able to get the best out of mental health services. It would be wonderful if our efforts, directly or indirectly, influence the development of services that effectively address the emotional, social and practical needs of people with mental health problems.

Richard Bentall
Pete Sanders
2020

Chapter 1
What this book aims to do

The *Straight Talking Introduction* series aims to introduce service users, carers, professionals and anyone else with an interest in mental health to important debates and controversies in the field that often don't get as much attention as they should. There are no easy answers, but once people are aware that there are other ways of describing and healing the very real and distressing experiences that are usually called 'mental illness', they may be able to make different choices and find better ways forward. The debates are important for all of us, not just those who have been given a psychiatric diagnosis, because they bring up important questions about how we all feel and behave, and the kind of societies we live in.

You may already be aware that the current mainstream way of describing psychological and emotional distress, which assumes that these experiences are the result of medical illnesses that need diagnosing and treating, has serious flaws. Not only does it lack evidence but it is found by many people to be unhelpful and even damaging. Of course, there is good mental health practice as well, some of which is referenced at the end of this book. But the limitations and potential harms of the diagnostic or 'medical model' approach are so serious that a growing number of people – service users and professionals – are calling for a complete alternative to the traditional medical way of thinking and practising.

This book is an introduction to one of those alternatives, the Power Threat Meaning Framework (PTMF). This ambitious project was co-produced by a group of psychologists and service users and published in January 2018. It is called a 'framework' because it is broader than any particular theory or model, although it shares features with some approaches you may already be familiar with. A framework is a kind of lens that guides how we think about and study a particular area – in this case, the various forms of troubling feelings and behaviour that are usually called 'mental illness'. For example, the medical framework is based on a set of ideas that suggests that we should look mainly to our brains and bodies to explain these experiences. The PTMF, on the other hand, unpicks these ideas and comes up with a very different set of principles that apply to every area of the field that we call 'mental health', including research, training, service design, mental health charities, peer support, welfare and housing agencies, the media, and policy-making at all levels.

For the purposes of this book, we have mainly focused on how people experiencing these various forms of troubling feelings and behaviour, and those working with or supporting them, can draw on the PTMF principles in order to gain a new perspective on the meanings and origins of emotional distress in all its forms. The PTMF documents are available to everyone, free, from the PTMF website,[1] and readers may wish to look at them in their original form.

The longer main document is titled *The Power Threat Meaning Framework: Towards the identification of patterns in emotional distress, unusual experiences and troubled or troubling behaviour, as an alternative to functional psychiatric diagnosis* (Johnstone & Boyle, 2018a) and is available online only. It sets out the problems of medicalisation and psychiatric diagnosis, outlines the principles, theories and research underpinning the framework, and reports the views of the consultancy group of service users and carers who gave feedback on the project. It also has a chapter on the wider practical implications of adopting a non-diagnostic approach. Readers wanting an in-depth understanding of the context, principles, research and practice from which the PTMF emerged may wish to read the main document in full. Alternatively, it may be useful to refer to specific chapters to find out more about particular aspects of the framework.

The shorter *Overview* document (Johnstone & Boyle, 2018b) consists mainly of Chapter 6 of the main document – that is,

---

1. See www.bps.org.uk/power-threat-meaning-framework and also Chapter 11 of this book.

the description of the framework itself. It also contains a guided discussion in Appendix 1, which takes readers through the core PTMF questions in a similar way to this book. Appendices 2–13 of the *Overview* describe a number of examples of current good practice that don't use diagnosis. In addition to being available online, the *Overview* can be ordered in hard copy, free of charge, from **www.membernetworkservices.org.uk**

However, these documents are long and quite dense in content and language. In this book we aim to provide a more accessible version of the PTMF ideas, along with suggestions about how the framework can be used in practice to create, or co-create, new and more hopeful narratives about people's lives and struggles. The principles of the PTMF apply to people who are in contact with mental health and related services, such as the criminal justice system, but also to anyone experiencing emotional difficulties, as we all do at some point in our lives.

The PTMF key ideas

Borrowing from the trauma-informed approach to emotional distress, the PTMF argues for a shift from asking, 'What's wrong with you?' to asking, 'What's happened to you?'

This means that the PTMF is based on these assumptions:

- Emotional distress, unusual experiences and many forms of troubled or troubling behaviour are understandable when viewed in the context of a person's relationships, life events and social circumstances and the standards and expectations we are all expected to live up to.

- There are strong links between personal/family/community distress and social contexts, especially where there is injustice and inequality.

- Different cultural expressions of distress should be accepted and respected.

- We all experience distress at times and the PTMF is about all of us. There is no separate group of people who are 'mentally ill'.

- We all make meaning out of what happens to us, and this shapes the way we experience and express our distress.

- With the right support, we can be active agents in our own lives, rather than seen as victims of a medical illness.

- The PTMF gives us tools to create new, hopeful narratives, or stories, about the reasons for our distress that are not based on psychiatric diagnosis. These narratives, which can take many forms, can help us find ways forward as individuals, families, social groups and whole societies.

We will expand on these ideas in Chapter 3.

Responses to the PTMF

The PTMF has sparked controversy and criticism from some quarters, partly because it poses such a major challenge to the usual way of thinking and practising (see Johnstone et al., 2019). At the same time, it has attracted a huge amount of interest, not just across the UK but further afield in Ireland, Spain, Denmark, Greece, Brazil, the US, Australia, New Zealand, India and South Korea. People who have attended PTMF workshops and training events or have come across the PTMF in other ways have said things like:

> 'Such an exciting and revolutionary new framework.'

> 'Absolutely makes sense and will definitely support my clinical practice and myself in my own life.'

> 'Just wonderful! Simple and clever at the same time.'

> 'An amazing project – this will help change people's lives for the better.'

> 'It makes so much sense to me.'

> 'Instils hope for change.'

By the end of this book, you will know enough about the PTMF to decide on your own view.

The structure of this book

- Chapter 2 starts with an overview of the problems and limitations of psychiatric diagnosis and the medical view of distress. While it may be quite challenging to read, we hope it will help you to understand why the PTMF was needed.

- Chapters 3, 4, 5, 6 and 7 expand on the PTMF core questions and the thinking behind them, and include optional exercises to explore how they might apply to your life or the life of someone you are working with or supporting.

- Chapter 8 describes the broad patterns of distress that underpin the framework.

- Chapter 9 consists of real-life examples of how to construct narratives based on PTMF ideas. By this stage, we hope readers will be interested in looking further into the deeply entrenched, mainly Western assumptions about the nature of distress and human relationships and experiences that underpin mainstream psychiatric practice, in order to understand why they have gained such a hold when there is no evidence to support them.

- Chapter 10 therefore returns to the broader context of the diagnostic model. This may provide a richer understanding of the framework and its context, and perhaps also of ourselves and the world we all inhabit.

- Chapter 11 summarises some of the wider implications and applications of the PTMF and provides references for the main PTMF documents and other resources.

The book tackles a number of complex themes, introducing and then returning to them over subsequent chapters so that they can be explored from various angles and in increasing depth. This means that the content has a more circular than linear structure.

We hope readers will end up with some answers to these questions:

- What are the problems with psychiatric diagnosis and the medical model of distress?

- What are the wider contexts and implications of the diagnostic debate?

- What are the core principles and ideas of the PTMF?

- How might the PTMF perspective apply in my life or the life of someone I am caring for, supporting, or working with?

- How might the PTMF influence thinking and practice more generally?

Some notes on the book

The scope of the PTMF

The PTMF is not intended to apply to the direct effects of conditions such as dementia, intellectual disabilities, neurological or neurodegenerative disorders or the physical consequences of stroke, brain injury, infections in older adults, and so on, although it might apply to some of their psychological and social consequences. Problems arising from the immediate effects of street drugs are also excluded. Autism has not been considered as a specific diagnosis; instead, readers may wish to look at the excellent debates about this complex topic at the Exeter University 'Exploring Diagnosis' project.[2]

Psychiatric drugs

The PTMF is not opposed to the use of psychiatric drugs for those who find them helpful, although it does note that it is rare for people to be fully informed about all their effects and their possible limitations and drawbacks. A useful guide to psychiatric drugs and their effects and to coming off them is Joanna Moncrieff's revised and updated *A Straight Talking Introduction to Psychiatric Drugs* (2020).

Please note that it is dangerous to reduce or stop your drugs without taking professional advice.

Language

Since we are proposing a non-medical perspective on distress, we don't use terms such as 'illness', 'disorder', 'symptom', 'patient' and so on, because they assume a medical viewpoint. We have indicated our reservations about this language by using speech marks, or by phrases such as '... was given a diagnosis of bipolar disorder'. Terms

---

2. See http://blogs.exeter.ac.uk/exploringdiagnosis

like 'distress', 'experience', 'service user' and 'mental health' are not entirely satisfactory but they are more neutral (but see Chapter 10 for a discussion about some of the disadvantages of the term 'mental health'). Your own choice of language is, of course, entirely up to you, and some people find medical terms useful and, indeed, necessary for some purposes. You can find a longer discussion on language in the PTMF *Overview* document, on pages 84–87.

Professions and their viewpoints

Psychiatrists are medical doctors who complete the initial five-year training at medical school and then go on to specialise in mental health, or one of its specialist fields such as children and young people, older adults or intellectual disabilities. Their training is mainly based on a diagnostic approach to mental, emotional and behavioural difficulties. They are able to prescribe psychiatric drugs and some have additional training in psychological therapies. Clinical psychologists do a degree in psychology and a three-year postgraduate training, and then work in specific clinical settings, including adult mental health, children and young people, older adults and intellectual disability (both authors of this book are clinical psychologists). They offer various types of counselling and talking therapy, including cognitive behavioural therapy (CBT). They also offer other services, including staff training and consultation and health education. Although, on the whole, clinical psychologists are more likely than psychiatrists to be critical of the diagnostic model of distress and to offer an alternative perspective, this is not true in every case. Some psychiatrists (for example, those who have contributed to the *Straight Talking Introduction* series) have been very outspoken about the limitations of diagnosis, and some psychologists strongly support it. Similarly, there is a range of opinions across professions such as nursing, social work, occupational therapy and so on, and service users themselves differ in their views. The debate is about ways of thinking, not about professional battles.

About the PTMF authors

Lucy Johnstone and Mary Boyle are the lead authors of the PTMF. The other main authors are John Cromby, Jacqui Dillon, David Harper, Peter Kinderman, Eleanor Longden, David Pilgrim, John

Read, and Kate Allsopp, who is research assistant to the project. They have, collectively, extensive experience in non-diagnostic perspectives on mental distress. This comes from clinical, teaching, training and research activities, and – particularly in the case of the two survivor members of the core group, Jacqui and Eleanor – from their own lived experience of extreme states of distress and their resulting contact with the mental health system.

We hope that, at the very least, this book brings you some new thoughts and insights. Good luck!

Chapter 2
The problems with diagnosis and why we need a different approach

Joe had been feeling anxious and panicky for quite a while but couldn't really say why. His GP referred him to his local NHS mental health service and he was diagnosed with generalised anxiety disorder. He was relieved to be told that, now he had a diagnosis, the right treatment could be started.

....

Amra is studying for a qualification as a mental health professional. She knows there are debates about the validity of diagnosis in mental health and would like to learn more. But her teaching is mainly organised around diagnostic categories, as are the services where she does her clinical placements, and most of the textbooks and research articles use the terminology of 'disorders'.

....

Ben was worried about his son's disruptive behaviour at home and school and that his schoolwork wasn't going as well as it used to. Looking for help online, he quickly came across information about 'conduct disorders'. He also found a website where he could complete a questionnaire about his son, and it would give him a psychiatric diagnosis.

These examples show how central psychiatric diagnosis is to our thinking about troubling emotions and behaviour. This seems to make sense. After all, if many forms of distress and troubling behaviour are similar to physical diseases or disorders, then we surely need a process that can distinguish one mental disorder from another and help us assign people to the right category. It also seems to make sense to use these categories to deliver services, teach students, communicate with the public and study the 'disorders' in order to find effective treatments.

All of this is supported by two very important publications that some readers will already be aware of. We will be referring to these quite often so it's worth giving some detail here. The first publication is the *Diagnostic and Statistical Manual of Mental Disorders,* or *DSM* (American Psychiatric Association (APA), 2013). It is now in its fifth edition (*DSM-5*) and contains lists of the criteria for applying diagnoses of one or more of around 400 types of 'mental disorders', such as 'schizophrenia', 'bipolar disorder' and 'major depressive disorder'. It is drawn up by a committee of the most senior mental health professionals in the US, most of whom are psychiatrists. The other publication is produced by the World Health Organization (WHO) and is called the *International Classification of Diseases*, or *ICD* (WHO, 2019). It is now in its 11th edition (*ICD-11*). The *ICD* covers all medical conditions – psychiatric disorders form just one section – but it is not intended as a diagnostic manual. Rather, it is intended to provide a way of ensuring that health information is recorded in standard formats worldwide and its uses also include the compilation of statistics about causes of death, studying patterns of health and illness across the world and allocating resources. The section on psychiatric 'disorders' is the only one that includes lists of diagnostic criteria. The reasons for this difference from other sections of the *ICD* will become clearer later.

The *DSM* and the psychiatric section of the *ICD* are based on the same principles and are similar, but not identical, in the 'disorders' they list and their diagnostic criteria. However the *DSM* is the most dominant worldwide, partly because many journals and research committees require the use of its categories rather than the *ICD* ones.

In spite of being so widely used, psychiatric diagnosis has been strongly and persistently criticised on many grounds. These include that psychiatric diagnosis medicalises thoughts, feelings and behaviour that are unusual or differ from the norm; that its categories are not evidence based and do not help us understand the causes of distress; that it sidelines people's life experience, can give them a negative, stigmatised identity and can rob them of hope that they will recover and have a better life again. And these problems are not getting any less – even some supporters of diagnosis have been very critical of the most recent *DSM*. For example, Dr Steven Hyman, former director of the US National Institute of Mental Health, has described *DSM-5* as 'totally wrong, an absolute scientific nightmare' (quoted in Belluck & Carey, 2013).[1]

We will go on to discuss these and other criticisms, but first we want to take a step back and address two questions:

- Why has psychiatric diagnosis encountered so many problems and so much criticism?

- Why do these problems seem so difficult to put right?

These questions are important because so much effort is still put into defending the system and trying to make it work. This is very costly in terms of time and money. It also makes it more difficult for service users, carers and the wider public to question diagnoses when the response is often along the lines of: 'The system may be flawed, but it's the best we've got, and we're constantly improving it.'

A good starting point in addressing fundamental questions about why the psychiatric diagnostic system is in such difficulties is to notice the implications of the fact that psychiatric diagnosis uses the same language as medical diagnosis, such as symptoms, signs, syndromes, disorders, diseases, comorbidity, and so on. This common language is supported by slogans such as that coined by the anti-stigma campaign charity Time to Change: 'As real as a broken arm.' Another slogan often used in anti-stigma campaigns is, 'Psychiatric illnesses are illnesses like any other.' All of this gives the impression that psychiatric diagnosis and medical diagnosis are the same kind of process, with the same goals and outcomes. In fact, the answers to our questions lie in the *differences* between the

---

1. The following can provide a more detailed understanding of the criticisms psychiatric diagnosis has faced and of the arguments in this chapter: Boyle (1999, 2002a); Johnstone, 2014; Kirk et al. (2013) and Timimi (2014), as well as Chapter 1 of the full PTMF document (Johnstone & Boyle, 2018a).

two processes. So, we'll first discuss what happens in diagnosis in other branches of medicine and then compare that with psychiatric diagnosis. This will take some unpacking, but we hope it will be helpful in showing why the problems facing psychiatric diagnosis are unlikely to be solved within the current system and why a very different approach is needed.

What is medical diagnosis?

We often talk about diagnosis as 'finding out what's wrong with someone' or 'finding out what disease or disorder someone has'. This isn't so much wrong as misleading and unhelpful in understanding what is actually going on.

It is more accurate to describe medical diagnosis as a process whereby doctors try to match a patient's 'complaints' (symptoms), and other abnormalities, with a pattern of bodily problems that researchers have already identified. 'Pattern' here means bodily problems that cluster together in a meaningful way, not just by coincidence. An example might be weight loss, tiredness, thirst and passing a lot of urine, which are all related to underlying problems with insulin production and the pancreas. This suggests a type of diabetes. We'll return later to this well-known example to illustrate key points about diagnosis.

Medical diagnosis, then, is a two-stage process. As patients, we only see the second stage where our problems are matched with an already known pattern. But first, researchers have to identify meaningful patterns (and doctors have to learn about them) before these patterns can be matched to a patient's problems. This first stage, of identifying patterns in the multitude of ways our bodies can go wrong, is far from easy. It has preoccupied those interested in the workings of the body for centuries. The research usually takes a long time and is conducted in laboratories and research centres, without much publicity, so that the public and even professionals may not know much about its importance, how it relates to medical diagnosis, and the difficulties it involves. This may not matter too much with medical diagnosis, which is less controversial. But it matters a great deal with psychiatric diagnosis, because it is also a two-stage process and many of the problems and criticisms it faces have their roots in the first stage, when psychiatric researchers try to find patterns in people's distress and troubling behaviour.

So, if we're to understand better why psychiatric diagnosis is in such difficulties and why no one seems able to fix them, it's worth looking more closely at how this essential first stage of the diagnostic process – pattern identification – works for medical diagnosis. We can then compare that with how the process has worked in psychiatric diagnosis and begin to see why its problems are so persistent.

The background to medical diagnosis: identifying patterns in bodily problems

It is always risky for medical researchers to try to identify patterns in bodily problems from people's subjective complaints alone – aches and pains, tiredness and thirst, for example – or from obvious features like rashes or lumps and bumps. We call these 'symptoms'. Because these experiences are very common, and have lots of causes, they will often appear together, just by coincidence. And some of them are very subjective – it can be difficult to know whether two people mean the same thing when they say they feel sick or are very thirsty. To get around these problems, medical researchers will try to find links between what seem to be clusters of symptoms and other physical characteristics or processes they can observe or measure more objectively. These are known as 'signs' and include levels of various blood chemicals, types of organ damage, presence of bacteria and so on.

Researchers will also look for evidence that the signs are playing some role in causing the symptoms. An example of this might be very high blood glucose levels, which can lead to someone needing to urinate a lot and feeling very thirsty. This kind of sequence gives researchers more confidence that they have identified a meaningful pattern and not just things that only appear together by chance.

When they've identified a basic pattern of signs and symptoms, researchers carry on finding out what is happening in the body so that they can understand better how the pattern came about. This often involves finding more signs, further back in the chain of causes. This is a continuous process, but at some point researchers give the pattern a semi-descriptive name – for example, diabetes, multiple sclerosis or cystic fibrosis. Sometimes a pattern is named after the person who first described it, such as Alzheimer or Parkinson.

Researchers have to have some idea of where to look in the body for these signs. This means being guided by evidence-based theory about how bodies function or malfunction. Researchers also have to be able to 'see' potential signs, and this often depends on technological advances, such as microscopes, stethoscopes, x-rays, magnetic resonance imaging (MRI) scans and chemical tests.

It's useful to return here to diabetes, because the gradual identification of the pattern we know as Type I diabetes is a good example of the complexities of pattern description. The ancient Greeks noted a cluster of thirst, frequent, very weak urine, tiredness and weight loss, which they called diabetes, meaning syphon or fountain. But it was not until the late 19th and 20th centuries that strong links were gradually established between this cluster and abnormalities in urine and blood glucose, insulin production and pancreatic functioning. We also know now that the original Greek cluster involved two separate patterns, with shared symptoms but different signs, now known as diabetes mellitus and diabetes insipidus (the latter is caused by abnormalities in the hormones that regulate kidney function). One reason for the long gap in progress was that doctors did not have the technology to access or measure internal bodily functions. Another was the lack of evidence-based theory about how bodies work, so that doctors had very little to guide them in where to look for the causes of these symptoms.

There has been rapid progress in both these areas in the last 150 years. As a result, medical researchers have been very successful at identifying what seem to be meaningful patterns of bodily problems. Some patterns are more complex and elaborate than others, and some, such as chronic fatigue syndrome, are at a very early stage of development. But none of the patterns are fixed. It is always possible that developments in technology, theory and evidence will enable the identification of new patterns and existing ones will be rearranged or abandoned, as has happened often in the past. The words we commonly use to talk about these patterns – such and such 'disease', 'illness' or 'disorder' – can give an impression of certainty that isn't really justified. Learning about these patterns and how to 'diagnose' them in their patients forms a large part of medical students' education.

From describing patterns to making a diagnosis

When medical researchers have described what they think is a meaningful pattern of bodily characteristics, then the signs, such as levels of glucose in the blood or certain kinds of cells in a tumour, become the key criteria for deciding if a particular patient's characteristics match this pattern. The diagnosis given to a patient is the name of whatever pattern the patient's problems match: e.g. diabetes, cancer, malaria or rheumatoid arthritis. Diagnostic criteria can change over time as researchers find out more about their initial pattern, often by discovering more about causes. Down's syndrome, for example, used to be diagnosed by delay in walking, talking and so on and by particular facial and other physical features. Nowadays, it's diagnosed by abnormalities in chromosomes (part of our genetic make-up).

When we report our symptoms to a doctor, their first thought will be: What patterns are these symptoms part of? The answer is probably 'several'. As we've seen, reporting thirst, going to the toilet a lot and tiredness could mean diabetes mellitus or diabetes insipidus. Or maybe you work in an overheated building, are working too hard and drinking too much coffee. The doctor will try to narrow this down by asking us about our symptoms but mainly by looking for signs, often through examinations or arranging tests. With luck, a match to a known pattern will be found fairly quickly. How much we can be told about our problems and how they can be helped depends on how much researchers know about the links from symptoms back to signs and how well they understand the biological processes involved in whatever pattern our signs and symptoms match. Of course, different patterns contain different amounts of information about causes. For some it is quite a lot, as in the example we've used of diabetes mellitus, or the pattern known as tuberculosis. Other patterns are not so informative: for example, the symptoms of 'irritable bowel syndrome' are so varied and not much is known about their causes. And for some people presenting with an array of signs, no clear match will be found.

Medical diagnosis, then, is not so much about 'discovering what disease someone is suffering from' or 'what illness they have' as about trying to match a person's bodily problems with a more general pattern already described by researchers. This is always in the hope of answering the questions: 'How have this person's problems come about?' and 'What can be done about them?'

How is psychiatric diagnosis different from medical diagnosis?

An obvious difference between psychiatric and medical diagnosis is that medical diagnosis focuses on bodily problems while psychiatric diagnosis focuses on people's thoughts, beliefs, feelings and actions. A less obvious but equally important difference is that psychiatric diagnoses are based on subjective complaints, either by the person themselves or those around them – what in medicine would be called 'symptoms'. These include experiences such as feeling very anxious, low in mood, or compelled to carry out rituals, or expressing very unusual beliefs, hearing voices or being reluctant to leave the house. (The few exceptions include diagnoses of some dementias or intellectual disabilities.)

The reason for this reliance on 'symptoms' is that, unlike medical researchers looking for patterns in people's bodily problems, psychiatric researchers have not been able to identify any 'signs' in their search for patterns in people's troubling thoughts, feelings and behaviour. In other words, there are no objective bodily characteristics that are consistently linked to these subjective complaints and seem to be causing them. This is what Dr David Kupfer, who chaired the taskforce that produced *DSM-5*, meant when he admitted:

> In the future, we hope to be able to identify disorders using biological and genetic markers that provide precise diagnoses that can be delivered with complete reliability and validity. Yet this promise, which we have anticipated since the 1970s, remains disappointingly distant. We've been telling patients for several decades that we are waiting for biomarkers. We're still waiting. (Kupfer, 2013)

'Biomarker' is another name for objective signs, such as genetic abnormalities or abnormalities in brain structures or chemistry – so-called chemical imbalances. In fact, psychiatric researchers have been trying, and failing, to find these biomarkers for more than a century.[2] Diagnostic manuals therefore just list clusters of 'symptoms' that are said to indicate various disorders, such as 'major depressive disorder', 'obsessive-compulsive disorder', 'schizophrenia', 'borderline personality disorder' and so on. Clinicians are encouraged to match people's emotional and behavioural difficulties to one of these clusters, and so 'make a diagnosis'. But these 'symptom' clusters are very unlikely to be valid patterns in any medical or scientific sense. This is not just for the reasons we discussed earlier – that 'symptoms' might cluster together by coincidence and that they rely on subjective judgements. It's also because turning our thoughts, feelings and behaviour into 'symptoms' and 'disorders' relies heavily on social customs and beliefs about how we ought to live our lives. We will return to these important points, but first we'll briefly describe how this problematic state of affairs has come about.

How have the differences between medical and psychiatric diagnosis come about?

The idea that a whole range of troubling emotions, psychological experiences and behaviours are symptoms of something going wrong with our bodies has a long history but really took hold from the late 19th and early 20th centuries. Obviously, things that go wrong with our bodies can influence our thoughts, feelings and behaviour: for example, tumours on the brain can cause aggression and confusion. But that is very different from assuming that many troubling emotions and behaviour are necessarily symptoms of 'mental diseases'. In fact, there was no direct evidence for this belief in the late 19th century, but it became popular for a variety of social, political, economic, theological and professional reasons. It was greatly encouraged by medicine's progress in identifying patterns in bodily problems and understanding some of their causes. Doctors assumed that the same progress would soon happen in relation to what they

---

2. There are frequent reports in the media of possible breakthroughs in finding these 'signs'. These have never come to anything, as we see from the fact that diagnosis still relies on subjective complaints. But the reports are important in maintaining a belief that psychiatric 'disorders' are similar to medical problems. See also Chapter 4 of this book.

judged to be abnormal feelings and behaviour, and that it would soon be possible to group them into distinct mental diseases or disorders with distinct biological causes (Boyle, 2002a; Scull, 1979).[3]

This progress did not happen. But clinicians still believed that these mental disorders must exist and that it was only a matter of time before their 'biomarkers' would be discovered. The result, as the 20th-century wore on, was that 'disorders' were 'identified' without evidence and clinicians chose which 'disorders' and which 'symptom' clusters to favour, according to their personal preferences. Inevitably, these clusters, or diagnostic criteria, varied in different parts of the country and across countries. This led to cynical comments about people being 'cured of schizophrenia' simply by taking a plane from New York to Stockholm, where diagnostic criteria were much narrower.

In 1980, the third edition of the *DSM* became the first manual to provide not just lists of 'mental disorders' but also their diagnostic criteria. *DSM-III* was published by the American Psychiatric Association as a way of dealing with what threatened to be diagnostic chaos and loss of professional status. This is also why, from its 10th edition in 1992, only the psychiatric section of the *ICD* has included diagnostic criteria. The medical sections do not need to include diagnostic criteria because what the *ICD* calls 'established criteria' for medical diagnoses are already available to doctors, through the processes of pattern identification we described earlier. So, the inclusion of diagnostic criteria for 'mental disorders' in the *DSM* and *ICD* did not represent any kind of scientific progress, although that was how it was presented; it was more an admission of lack of progress (Boyle, 2002a). What happened was that 'mental disorders' and their 'official' diagnostic criteria were, and still are, voted into existence by committees on the basis of whatever the committees decided were symptoms. As Professor Donald Klein, a leader in developing diagnostic criteria, put it:

---

3. Medicine's success in describing patterns of infectious diseases, especially the description of the pattern we know as syphilis, with its mixture of physical and mental features, was a significant source of the hope of finding similar patterns of 'mental disease'.

... we were forced to rely on clinical consensus, which, admittedly, is a very poor way to do things... We thrashed it out, basically. We had a three-hour argument... If people were still divided, the matter would be eventually decided by a vote. (Quoted in Davies, 2013, pp.29–30)

Renee Garfinkel, a psychologist who took part in *DSM* meetings, puts it more plainly:

What I saw happening on these committees wasn't scientific – it more resembled a group of friends trying to decide where they want to go for dinner. One person says, 'I feel like Chinese food', and another person says, 'No, no, I'm really more in the mood for Indian food', and finally, after some discussion and collaborative give-and-take, they all decide to go have Italian. (Quoted in Davies, 2013, p.30)

This situation has not changed since 1980, as we saw from David Kupfer's comment on *DSM-5*, in spite of a major update of the psychiatric section of the *ICD* and three revisions of the *DSM*.[4] A key question, which we'll return to at the end of the chapter, is whether the situation is ever likely to change.

What happens when people are given a psychiatric diagnosis?

All of this inevitably causes problems when psychiatric diagnoses are used in mental health services. For example...

Diagnoses are based on subjective judgements and social norms

We've noted two major differences between medical and psychiatric diagnoses. First, that psychiatric diagnosis focuses

---

4. See Boyle (2002a), Kirk et al. (2013) and Kutchins et al. (1997) for discussions of the process of developing diagnostic criteria across editions of the *DSM*. UK clinicians sometimes defend their diagnostic practice, saying that they use the *ICD* and not the *DSM*. But the psychiatric chapter of the *ICD* is developed in the same way as the *DSM* and with all the same problems; it is just as dependent on subjective judgements and social norms. However, being less well known, the *ICD* is less often targeted for criticism.

on people's thoughts, feelings and actions; second, with the few exceptions that overlap with neurology, these diagnoses are not based on more objective physical signs because psychiatric researchers have failed to find any. Together, these differences mean that the transformation of people's thoughts, feelings and behaviour into symptoms and illness categories has to be based on subjective social judgements about what are believed to be normal ways of thinking, feeling and behaving.

It's not surprising, then, that terms like 'excessive', 'inappropriate' or 'out of proportion' are common in psychiatric diagnostic criteria. These are obviously meant to convey abnormality without saying what is normal. However, diagnostic criteria also often include specific numbers: for example, the person must show a specified number from a longer list of 'symptoms', or must feel or do something at least once a day or have shown the 'symptoms' for a specified length of time. All of this gives a false impression of scientific exactness, when there is no reliable evidence to support any set of numbers over another.[5]

Relying on subjective judgements like these means relying on social norms. Deciding whether someone is having 'unusual perceptual experiences' or 'excessive guilt', or whether they are 'often touchy and easily annoyed' or have 'inflated self-esteem' or even 'deficient erotic thoughts or fantasies'[6] depends on judgements about how we *should* think, feel or behave in certain circumstances. Diagnostic manuals acknowledge this indirectly. For example, *DSM-5* claims that our feelings or actions should not count as symptoms of mental disorder if they are normal, expected responses to particular circumstances. *ICD-11*'s description of 'prolonged grief disorder' is a good example of this:

> The grief response has persisted for an atypically long period of time following the loss (more than 6 months at

---

5. See Boyle (2002a, p.125) for a discussion of the various time criteria for 'schizophrenia' diagnosis.

6. These are listed as potential symptoms of 'schizophrenia', 'major depressive disorde', 'oppositional defiant disorder', 'bipolar 1 disorder' and 'male hypoactive sexual desire disorder'.

a minimum) and clearly exceeds expected social, cultural or religious norms for the individual's culture and context. (WHO, 2019)

So, in order to count as a symptom, what we feel or do should not be understandable or expected in our social context. But what *is* a 'normal' or 'expected' response to having insecure work, being in an abusive relationship, having parents who neglected you, living in a consumerist society, being racially or sexually harassed, or losing a beloved partner, child or pet? And who decides? The answers will depend on who you ask, where they live, and at what historical time. The answers can also tell us more about people's limited knowledge, imagination and empathy than about the causes of feelings and behaviour.

Just as important, the answers can tell us about power structures in a society. For example, two diagnoses that are mainly or only given to women – borderline personality disorder and premenstrual dysphoric disorder – list 'inappropriate anger' or 'marked anger' as diagnostic criteria. Yet there is evidence that women given these diagnoses have good reason to be angry about their situations, which often involve experiences of powerlessness and subordination (Newnham & Janka, 2014; Ussher, 2004; Johnstone & Boyle, 2018a, Chapter 4). Not being understandable to those around you may be a cause for concern or a signal that you need help, but it is not reliable evidence that your behaviour is a symptom of a biologically based 'disorder'.

Diagnostic criteria also often say that the person's so-called symptoms should cause them distress or interfere with day-to-day functioning. But how we feel about our own emotions and behaviour also depends on social norms and expectations about how we *should* feel and behave, what we should and shouldn't be able to cope with and what our reactions to events might mean. How much 'symptoms' interfere with day-to-day life will also depend on how well off we are, if we have a job or not, what that job is, where we live, and how those around us respond to our behaviour or distress.

Given all this, we should not be surprised that what are said to be symptoms of mental disorders tend to reflect current social concerns. 19th and early 20th century 'mental disorders' included homosexuality and 'drapetomania' – a condition said to cause Black slaves to run away from their 'owners'. They also included 'nymphomania', for women who enjoyed sex too much. None of these appears in current manuals, and modern diagnoses of women's 'sexual dysfunctions' only include enjoying sex too little. Sociologist Bruce Cohen has analysed the contents of the *DSM* from its first edition in 1952 to the fifth in 2013. He describes the large expansion in what counts as unacceptable or potentially 'symptomatic' behaviour in schools and workplaces, and in children more generally, with each edition of the *DSM* (Cohen, 2016). We can see, for example, that diagnostic criteria such as 'often arguing with authority figures' or 'having poor time management' or 'making careless mistakes in school work or at work' (all listed as potential symptoms of 'oppositional defiant disorder' and 'attention deficit/hyperactivity disorder') are not very compatible with target-driven schooling or the pressure to be productive at work.[7]

None of this means that emotional or behaviour difficulties are 'just' social judgements. Our emotions and behaviour may at times be extremely distressing and troubling to us and/or those around us. But there is a big difference between acknowledging the reality of distress and troubling behaviour and presenting social judgements about it as if they were illness categories. The norms and values underlying 'mental disorder' diagnoses are also often those of higher class, White, Western men, so these judgements are more of a problem for people from groups who have less say in the creation of dominant social norms. This includes women, children, people on low incomes and people from African, Caribbean and Asian heritage living in White-dominated societiess, all of whom are over-represented in Western 'mental disorder' statistics. It is also a problem when psychiatric diagnosis is exported to non-Western countries, for example through the Global Mental Health Movement. We will return to these important issues in Chapters 8 and 10.

---

7. See also Chapter 4 in this book.

Clinicians disagree about when to give a diagnosis

If diagnoses are based on subjective judgements and social norms, clinicians are likely to disagree on which diagnosis to give. This is known as unreliability and is a long-standing problem of psychiatric diagnostic systems (Kirk & Kutchins, 1992). It seems to be getting worse with each new edition of the *DSM*,[8] and even *DSM* supporters have been critical. Dr Allen Frances, chair of the committee that drew up the fourth edition in 1994, commented on the fifth edition, published in 2013:

> [The American Psychiatric Association] flunked – instead of admitting that its reliability results were unacceptable… the goal posts were moved. Declaring… that previous expectations were too high, *DSM-5* announced it would accept agreements among raters that were sometimes barely better than two monkeys throwing darts at a diagnostic board. (Frances, 2013, p.175)

People may be given multiple diagnoses

As people move through mental health services, it's not unusual for their diagnosis to change or for them to collect several diagnoses (known as 'co-morbidity'). This can be confusing and distressing, leaving people feeling that no one understands their problems or, perhaps worse, that they have so many disorders it is difficult to see a way forward. In fact, the problem lies in the diagnostic system. This situation is inevitable if reliability is low and clinicians cannot agree on what illness someone is supposed to have. It also arises from the fact that our responses to very difficult life circumstances don't fall into artificial 'disorder' categories. For example, many – if not most – people who are given a diagnosis of a mood disorder such as 'major depressive disorder' will also meet the criteria for an

---

8. Research on agreement between clinicians on *DSM-5* diagnoses found that for 'major depressive disorder' it was 0.28 and for 'generalised anxiety disorder', 0.20 (where 1 equals perfect agreement and 0 equals no agreement between clinicians' judgements). Agreement on other common diagnoses was not much better: 'schizophrenia' was 0.46 and 'borderline personality disorder' 0.54 (Regier et al., 2013).

'anxiety disorder'.[9] This is not because they are suffering from two mental disorders but because the kind of circumstances that make us feel very anxious and apprehensive can also make us feel hopeless and despairing, especially if we can't see any way of dealing with them or if nothing we've tried seems to work. There are similar overlaps across many other categories, so that people can often seem to 'match' at least some of the criteria for more than one 'disorder'. We will return to this point in Chapters 7 and 8.

Diagnosis is not an explanation

We often see diagnoses used as an explanation for how people feel or behave: he cries a lot because he's depressed; she hears voices because she has schizophrenia. One diagnosis may also be used to explain another. For example, in an online comment column on mental health problems, a clinician claimed that a woman's 'psychotic episode was a consequence of [her] bipolar affective disorder, which had been triggered by a bout of postnatal depression' (Gerada, 2018). But psychiatric diagnosis cannot explain distress because the argument is always circular: 'Why does she hear voices?' 'Because she suffers from schizophrenia.' 'How do you know she suffers from schizophrenia?' 'Because she hears voices.' And using one diagnosis to explain another is just as circular. There is no possibility of finding an exit from the circles through identifying signs, as is possible with physical disorders: 'Investigations have shown that her headache is caused by a tumour in her brain' or, 'His stomach pain is caused by an ulcer.' Some medical diagnoses, such as irritable bowel syndrome or eczema, don't explain symptoms either. But this is very different from having an entire system based on circular explanation. If we want to understand why someone might feel or behave as they do, we need to move away from a diagnostic model.

---

9. *DSM-5* claims that 'major depressive disorder' frequently co-occurs not just with 'anxiety disorders' such as 'panic disorder' and 'obsessive-compulsive disorder' but also with 'anorexia nervosa', 'bulimia nervosa', 'borderline personality disorder' and 'substance-related disorders' (APA, 2013, p.168).

Diagnosis favours drugs as the first line of help

The names of many psychiatric drugs, such as 'antidepressants', 'antipsychotics', 'anxiolytics' and 'mood stabilisers', suggest that they are treatments for specific disorders. There is no evidence for this – the names owe more to marketing than science. There is also no evidence that the drugs target an underlying biological process, such as a so-called chemical imbalance. In practice, the same drug may be recommended for several different 'disorders'. For example, 'antipsychotic' drugs have been recommended for people given diagnoses of 'schizophrenia', 'bipolar disorder', 'personality disorder' and 'attention deficit hyperactivity disorder', as well as anxiety and depression. In the same way, 'antidepressant' drugs have been recommended not just for complaints of depression but also for diagnoses of 'borderline personality disorder', 'obsessive-compulsive disorder', 'panic disorder' and fear of social situations (Moncrieff, 2008a; 2013). In her book, *A Straight Talking Introduction to Psychiatric Drugs*, psychiatrist Joanna Moncrieff (2020) argues that these and other psychiatric drugs are not specific 'treatments' but have much more general brain-altering effects. Some effects – helping us sleep, calming us down, making us feel more alert – can be welcome and help people cope; other effects are unwelcome and even damaging. This applies to many brain-altering substances. Alcohol is often called a 'social lubricant', but we don't recommend it as a treatment for 'social anxiety disorder' or claim that it corrects a 'chemical imbalance' that causes 'social anxiety'. The idea of drugs as able to target and treat specific 'disorders' can also make it difficult to question their costs and benefits and to see them as a short-term option that may help some people, rather than as a lifetime necessity.

Diagnosis does not remove stigma and discrimination

Anti-stigma campaigns are often based on the claim that 'mental illness is an illness like any other', in the belief that this can reduce shame and promote more positive attitudes. Unfortunately, the evidence points in the other direction: diagnostic 'explanations' can increase stigma and discrimination (Kvaale et al., 2013; Read et al., 2013). It is not difficult to see why. Explanations based on 'mental disorders' that apparently make people behave in unusual ways can reinforce stereotypes of difference, unpredictability and even dangerousness. And the fact that these 'explanations' also mystify the nature and causes of people's difficulties potentially increases fear and stigma for the person themselves and those around them.

Diagnosis can remove meaning

Receiving a psychiatric diagnosis changes what people feel and do into something they have (such as a brain disorder) or are (such as a damaged or defective kind of personality). It replaces one possible way of looking at things ('Your distress is understandable, given your life story') with another ('Your distress is a symptom of an illness'). Some people welcome the second interpretation because, in attributing how they are feeling to a physical illness, it seems to have fewer negative meanings, such as that they are weak, bad or a failure. For others, receiving a diagnosis creates feelings of damage, hopelessness and exclusion and limits possibilities for change (see Johnstone, 2014, Chapter 6). More generally, diagnostic understandings can make our distress seem meaningless by cutting its links with our social contexts and relationships and focusing instead on what might be 'wrong' with our brains and bodies. This makes it easier to overlook the harmful impact of economic and social policies, negative life experiences or just taken-for-granted aspects of everyday life such as gender-role expectations or working long hours.

What are the implications?

Psychiatric diagnosis doesn't simply claim to distinguish one 'mental disorder' from another. As we've seen, it is a way of thinking about distress and troubling behaviour that underlies the entire system of mental health services, professional training, teaching and research. (We discuss this in more detail in Chapter 11.) Yet the problems we have outlined above mean that psychiatric diagnosis is not able to fulfil any of the main purposes of diagnosis that might justify all of this – it doesn't place people in separate, meaningful groups; it doesn't help us identify causes of distress, and it doesn't tell us how we can reliably help. Dr Thomas Insel, former head of the US National Institute of Mental Health, has spelled out the scale of this failure:

I spent 13 years at NIMH really pushing on the neuroscience and genetics of mental disorders, and when I look back on that I realize that, while I think I succeeded at getting lots of really cool papers published by cool scientists at fairly large costs – I think $20 billion –I don't think we moved the needle in reducing suicide, reducing hospitalizations, improving recovery for the tens of millions of people who have mental illness. (Quoted in Henriques, 2017)

What should we do instead? It is sometimes argued that the problems facing psychiatric diagnosis are just because 'mental disorders' are so complex and it is hard to measure what is going on in the brain, but with enough time and money, we will find 'biomarkers for mental disorders'.[10] This does seem unlikely. Let's go back to the questions we posed at the beginning of the chapter: Why has psychiatric diagnosis encountered so many problems and so much criticism? And, Why are these problems so resistant to attempts to resolve them? A key part of the answer is that psychiatric researchers have taken it for granted that the methods and assumptions used by medical researchers in identifying patterns in bodily problems can be applied to finding similar patterns – of symptoms and signs – in our 'abnormal' thoughts, feelings and behaviour.

But what if distress and troubling behaviour are *not* diagnosable 'illnesses like any other' and need to be understood in a very different way? Seen from this perspective, researchers have failed to find signs or biomarkers of 'mental disorders' precisely because they are not there. The often-expressed hope of 'precision diagnosis' based on blood tests or brain scans will always be unfulfilled. In other words, these researchers have been looking for meaningful patterns of distress through the wrong lens or framework and, predictably, have not found them.

If we try to understand our troubling thoughts, feelings and behaviour from a medical perspective, we miss so much that is important about them. Our body parts, such as organs, limbs,

---

10. See the full PTMF document, pages 16–18 and 33–35, and Chapter 7 in Mary Boyle's book *Schizophrenia: A scientific delusion?* (2002a) for more detailed discussion of some defences of diagnosis and suggested alternatives.

circulatory systems and so on, don't have language, culture, friends or families; they don't reminisce with others about the past or plan the future. They don't do things with a specific goal in mind. They don't create stories or social groups; they don't feel love, hate, loneliness or despair. They don't try to make sense of their experiences. Yet these characteristics of us as *persons* are vital to understanding our distress and troubling behaviour, not as symptoms of illness but as highly meaningful responses to difficult life experiences. Of course, our distress has biological aspects, as all our experiences do, but, as we'll describe, these aspects are inseparable from our social and relational lives. The PTMF shows that, when we approach distress with these human characteristics in mind, very different kinds of patterns emerge that suggest very different approaches to the dilemmas faced by people like Joe, Amra and Ben at the start of the chapter. We hope these ideas will also be useful to readers of this book.

Chapter 3
Introducing the Power Threat Meaning Framework

The previous chapter described the many problems with the diagnostic approach, and the growing tide of criticism it is attracting. One result of these controversies was an official statement by the Division of Clinical Psychology (DCP) of the British Psychological Society (BPS), representing the UK's 10,000 clinical psychologists. In 2013, at the same time as the publication of *DSM-5*, the DCP released a document formally calling for 'a paradigm shift in relation to the experiences that these diagnoses refer to, towards a conceptual system that is no longer based on a "disease" model' (DCP, 2013). In other words, this professional body made a bold public statement that the diagnostic approach is not fit for purpose and needs to be replaced.

The DCP document also recommended, among other things, that there should be 'work, in conjunction with service users, on developing a multi-factorial and contextual approach, which incorporates social, psychological and biological factors' (p.1). This was the context in which a group of psychologists and service users was funded by the DCP to develop the principles of an alternative to the diagnostic approach. The total project group eventually numbered about 40 people, approximately a third of whom had experience of using psychiatric services. Five years later, in January 2018, the result of this project, The Power Threat Meaning Framework (PTMF), was launched.

The PTMF is not an official DCP or BPS position, and nor is it a plan or set of recommendations for services, or for anything else.

Rather, it is an optional set of ideas or a conceptual resource that people may or may not find useful. Its core principles are based on a very extensive overview of the evidence, and the published documents describing it (Johnstone & Boyle, 2018a, 2018b) represent the first stage of the project. We hoped that people from various backgrounds would be interested in trying out these ideas in their own settings, either to support existing good practice or to develop new ways forward, and this is what has happened. Their experiences and evaluations are feeding back into the development of the PTMF and providing further evidence and support for the PTMF perspective. This is the second, ongoing stage of the project (see Chapter 11 for more details).

As we saw in Chapter 1, the PTMF perspective can be summarised in the words of the survivor slogan: 'Instead of asking what is wrong with me, ask what has happened to me.' The PTMF expands this into the following core questions:

- 'What has happened to you?' (How is *power* operating in your life?)

- 'How did it affect you?' (What kind of *threats* does this pose?)

- 'What sense did you make of it?' (What is the *meaning* of these situations and experiences to you?)

- 'What did you have to do to survive?' (What kinds of *threat response* are you using?)

- 'What are your strengths?' (What access to *power resources* do you have?)

- … and to integrate all the above: *'What is your story?'*

In fact, these are overlapping questions. In Chapters 4 to 9, we will see that you cannot ask about power without implying the existence of threat, and you cannot talk about threat without suggesting meaning, and so on. However, they are a convenient way of summarising the main themes of the PTMF and the aspects of people's lives that need to be considered. In this and the following chapters, we will explain what is meant by them and illustrate how they can help us to create new narratives about our struggles and our lives.

The core principles of the PTMF

Below is a more detailed description of the PTMF key ideas that were listed in Chapter 1. We can see that they are fundamentally different from those underpinning the diagnostic model. We will draw out their implications in the rest of the book and show how they can lead to very different ways forward.

- Emotional distress, like all human experiences, is experienced and expressed partly through our bodies. The PTMF main document has a detailed overview of relevant biological and evolutionary factors. But, while all our experiences have physical aspects, not all distress is best understood as a medical illness with mainly biological causes and treatments. This is particularly true of the effects of the traumas and adversities that occur in many people's lives.

- We will never be able to make simple links between 'This happened to me' and 'This is the result'. This is because, when things go wrong in our lives, the outcome is shaped by a multitude of factors, including the support we get and the sense we make of the situation. No one is doomed to long-term emotional distress or 'mental illness' because of difficult life experiences.

- The origins of the experiences we call 'mental health problems' are, when traced back to their roots, social and political, which is why the PTMF has implications far beyond one-to-one therapy and support. Judgements about how we ought to think, feel and behave are based on values, not on objective medical criteria, and those values draw on deeply held assumptions about the kinds of people we should be and the kind of lives we should be living. Feeling that you are unable to conform to or live up to these expectations can cause great distress, even if you have not experienced obvious traumas or adversity.

- Expressions and experiences of distress will always be shaped by the culture in which they arise. Rather than exporting the diagnostic model across the world, Westernised societies have much to learn from non-Western understandings of distress and healing.

- Human beings are fundamentally social beings, not separate individuals making their own purely personal journeys through their lives. Distress arises within and can only be healed through our personal and social relationships and our wider communities.

- Human beings have 'agency' – in other words, they are not just passively acted on by outside forces, as in the case of an infection that (say) attacks your lungs and makes you cough. Of course, we may face very severe constraints, such as not being able to afford good housing or enough to eat. At the same time, we still retain the ability to make some choices in our lives, even if our options are very limited.

- The responses described in psychiatry as 'symptoms' are actually our best attempt to survive difficult situations, both past and present. They represent what people *do* in the face of hardship, consciously or otherwise, not an illness that they *have*.

- Human beings are meaning-makers, and these meanings arise out of our experiences, our relationships, and our social and cultural contexts. We all try to make sense of our circumstances, good and bad, and this shapes how we are affected by them and how we respond.

- One of the most damaging effects of psychiatric diagnosis is to obscure personal meanings. If hearing voices, having mood swings or starving yourself are seen as 'symptoms' of an 'illness', then there is not much reason to explore your life experiences and the sense you made of them. The PTMF, in contrast, argues that we need to move away from the medical approach and place the central focus on meaning, narrative and personal experience.

- One of the implications of these core principles is that *stories and narratives of all kinds can replace psychiatric diagnosis.*

To bring the PTMF ideas to life, you may want to reflect on the core questions as you read the next few chapters. We have suggested a series of short exercises to help you to do this. You can use them in relation to your own life (whether or not you have been diagnosed with mental health problems). You can also draw on the ideas in your professional work with clients or service users. By the time you have worked through all the questions, you will, we hope, have created a narrative about your life and your struggles, or those of the person you are working with, that may be different in some ways from the one that is currently held and may suggest new ways forward. (Some groups, such as children, people with intellectual disabilities, or older adults with cognitive impairments might need extra support with using the PTMF materials – see Chapter 11.)

There is no need to do the exercises in order to understand the PTMF, but if you do want to try them out, please read the section below. Other readers can skip this and go on to Chapter 4.

Exercise 1
Preparing to reflect on the PTMF core questions

If you, or someone you are working with, decide to try these exercises, we strongly suggest that you take steps to make them as safe and manageable as possible. We hope you will find the process helpful and enlightening. At the same time, the questions inevitably touch on difficult and upsetting events and circumstances, and if this feels in any way uncomfortable or unsafe, we strongly recommend you don't continue and, if you feel it is necessary, seek support, whether from mental health professionals or from family, friends or the sources of help listed at the end of this chapter.

As we have said, there is no correct, prescribed wording or order for exploring the PTMF questions. They are intended as suggestions for areas to reflect on, not as a formal assessment. The first PTMF core question expands 'What has happened to you?' into 'How is power operating in your life?' because that is the aspect most often missing from psychiatric and some psychological approaches to distress. However, as previously stated, since each of the questions arises out of the others, you can take any of them as a starting point. Like the structure of this book, you may find yourself returning to themes rather than working through them in a set order.

Here are some suggestions for making this process as safe and manageable as possible if you are the person who is exploring their story.

- Make a list of people or organisations who can offer support if it is needed and/or ask one of those people (such as a close friend or family member) to be with you as you reflect on the questions. If you are in contact with mental health or related services, it may be helpful to tell a professional you know and trust that you are planning to explore these areas. They may be willing to support you through this process or discuss your thoughts and reflections with you afterwards.

- Choose a time when your life is reasonably settled and stable and you are not dealing with major stresses.

- Make a list of strategies for managing strong emotions, in case you find the exercises upsetting. The link below takes you to a 'Stabilisation Pack' produced by the Cwm Taf Morgannwg Psychological Services department in conjunction with service users.[1] We suggest you read the leaflets in the self-help section of the pack and choose and practise some strategies, so you know what works best for you. Of course, you may already have your own preferred ways of managing difficult or overwhelming feelings.

- Take the exercises as slowly as you like. Have a break if you need one. Afterwards, you may want to do something relaxing (spend time in nature, have a hot bath) or releasing (allow yourself to cry, go on a walk or a run) or distracting (watch TV or a film, meet a friend), whatever feels most useful.

Exercise 2

'What are your strengths?' (What power resources do you have?)

For the purposes of this book, we suggest you start with the question about strengths, or (in PTMF language) power resources. This list of strengths and resources may include people who care for you or the person you are working with, aspects of your/their identity that you/they feel good about, skills and values that are important to you/them, and so on. Some suggestions are given below. Work through

---

1. http://cwmtaf.wales/services/mental-health/stabilisation-pack

them at your own pace, making a note of any that seem to apply to you. As with all the questions, you may want to return to the list later if you have additional thoughts.

The PTMF questions and prompts can also be accessed online as part of the PTMF 'guided discussion' in the main document.[2] The template on page 91 of the guided discussion can be used to jot down ideas as you go along, if you find that useful. Please note that it doesn't matter too much which response goes under which heading – the main aim is to encourage ideas and reflections in order to build a story.

Strengths and power resources

Your strengths and power resources might include:

- loving and secure relationships in early life. Even if not everyone offered you this, one or two people (relatives and teachers, for example) can make a big difference

- supportive partners, family and friends in your life now

- social contacts such as neighbours, the local community, a peer group, online support groups and friends on social media. These can give a sense of belonging

- professional support (such as mental health/advice/housing/counselling services)

- access to leisure and educational opportunities

- having access to information/knowledge of various kinds, including alternative views on mental health

- valued aspects of identity (for example, taking pride in being a woman, or a parent, or having Black or mixed heritage, or a particular work role, and so on)

- skills and abilities, such as intelligence, resourcefulness, determination and particular talents

- physical resources, such as appearance, strength, physical health and sporting ability

---

2. See www.bps.org.uk/sites/www.bps.org.uk/files/Policy/Policy%20-%20Files/PTM%20Guided%20Discussion.pdf

- belief systems and rituals, such as religious or spiritual practices, community ceremonies and so on

- community involvement, such as churchgoing, volunteering, political activities

- connections to nature and the natural world – such as looking after pets, spending time in the countryside.

You might want to think about some of the following ways of building on resources and strengths:

- managing emotions by releasing, expressing or processing feelings (for example, writing, exercise, talking therapies, body therapies, creativity and the arts, compassion-focused approaches, mindfulness, meditation)

- self-care (for example, good nutrition, exercise, rest, alternative therapies)

- using or finding additional relationships for emotional support, protection, validation

- other activities, ceremonies and interventions that are culturally meaningful.

In the longer term, some people may find empowerment and strength from building on the following:

- finding new social roles and activities

- getting involved in campaigning and activism

- creating/finding new narratives/meanings/beliefs/values for the life you want to lead.

Chapters 4, 5, 6, and 7 will focus on the rest of the PTMF questions and the ideas and evidence that underpin them. Chapter 8 will look at what we call 'general patterns' that support personal narratives, and Chapter 9 gives some examples of what your story might look like at the end of the whole process.

Chapter 4
'What has happened to you?' (How is power operating in your life?)

This chapter explores the first of the PTMF core questions. Because power, in both its positive and negative senses, is a central aspect of all our lives, we wanted the PTMF to put it first and foremost. Understanding the operation of power is complex, but we hope this chapter will repay careful reading. We start with the first part of the question, 'What has happened to you?', before going on to explore power.

We're often told that 'mental health problems can affect anyone'.[1] In some ways this is true, because emotional distress, unusual experiences and troubled or troubling behaviour are universal and all of us will experience distress at some time in our lives. But in other ways the claim can be misleading, because it is not just 'anyone' who enters mental health services or gets psychiatrically diagnosed. Our chances of these outcomes vary greatly with our life circumstances – with what has happened to us. Before we discuss the evidence, it is very important to emphasise that, in this section, we are describing an overall picture about groups or populations. This doesn't tell us how any particular individual will be affected, and people's responses vary a great deal.

We can start with the fact that there is a large amount of evidence about the circumstances and events most strongly linked with many forms of distress and troubling behaviour. These

---

1. The 'can affect anyone' claim is bolstered by the assumption that 'mental disorders' are separate from us, that they 'happen' to us, rather than referring to understandable reactions to difficult life experiences (see Chapter 10).

include childhood sexual, physical and emotional abuse; child physical and emotional neglect; domestic violence; being in care; bullying; rape and sexual assault; poverty and low social class; unemployment; racial, sexual and other forms of discrimination; living in a country with high income inequalities; poor housing; living in a high crime area or areas of war and conflict, and being a refugee.[2]

The figures are very striking, especially in relation to childhood experience.[3] One study reported that people who had experienced any of a range of adversities in childhood, such as sexual, physical or emotional abuse, losing a parent, being taken into care or bullying, were almost three times more likely to receive a diagnosis of a 'psychotic disorder' (Varese et al., 2012). The likelihood of this outcome rises with the extent and severity of abuse and adversity. People who had endured three kinds of abuse were 18 times more likely to be diagnosed as 'psychotic', while for those suffering the severest kinds of abuse, the risk rose to 48 times (Janssen et al., 2004). Another study reported that people who had five or more 'adverse childhood experiences' (ACEs) were 10 times more likely to be prescribed 'antipsychotic' drugs and 17 times more likely to be prescribed 'mood stabilising' drugs (Anda et al., 2007). Studies of people admitted to psychiatric facilities suggest that the majority have experienced some kind of childhood abuse or neglect (Read et al., 2005; McFetridge et al., 2015). More generally, violence against girls and women is recognised worldwide as one of the leading causes of psychological harm (UNFPA, n.d.). These experiences also affect people's physical health, which in turn can increase their psychological distress.

Even if you have not experienced obvious trauma, such as child sexual or physical abuse, belonging to a disadvantaged group can increase the risk of being psychiatrically diagnosed or experiencing some form of distress (see Johnstone & Boyle, 2018a, Chapter 4). For example, women overall have a higher

---

2. We discuss this evidence in detail in Chapter 4 of the main PTMF document.

3. Important evidence about the impact of childhood adversity comes from the ACE (adverse childhood experience) studies, which gathered information from more than 17,000 participants over 15 years. Researchers looked at the impact of a range of childhood abuse, neglect and family dysfunction on both physical and mental health in adulthood.

rate of mental health problems than men, and people of African or African Caribbean ancestry living in the UK are between six and nine times more likely than White people to get a diagnosis of 'schizophrenia'. There is consistent evidence linking this to racial discrimination. Being poor is linked to a whole range of mental health difficulties and economic recessions are associated with higher suicide rates, especially for men.[4] Living in a country with high inequalities in income and wealth, such as the UK or the US, can also have damaging effects. In their books *The Spirit Level* (2010) and *The Inner Level* (2018), epidemiologists Richard Wilkinson and Kate Pickett argue that having a large gap between the richest and poorest in society increases people's worries about their social position, with some more likely to feel inferior and ashamed in comparison with others. A large wealth gap also leads to increased crime and violence (perhaps as a way of getting respect); lower educational achievement; less chance of increasing your income, class and status, so that people have less hope for their and their children's future, and loss of trust and cohesion in and across communities.

All of this certainly justifies asking 'What has happened to you?' instead of 'What's wrong with you?' This change of perspective immediately shifts our attention away from (supposedly) malfunctioning minds and brains to the wider social world and the ways it can harm us. But making the change is not straightforward. Mental health professionals often say that of course they ask about people's histories and life events. Unfortunately, it is possible to ask someone in distress 'What's happened to you?', and still be more or less where we started, talking about 'illness', 'diagnoses' and 'mental disorders'.

A common way of doing this is through the popular 'biopsychosocial model'. This was originally suggested as a way of integrating biological, psychological and social aspects of physical health problems. It was then extended to emotional and psychological distress. However, clinical psychologist John Read points out that the supposed integration 'is more illusion than reality'; the emphasis is still on biological abnormalities as the

---

4. The supporting research for these can be found in Chapter 4 of the main PTMF document, in the sections on gender, 'race' and ethnicity and social class and poverty.

underlying causes of 'mental disorders', he argues (Read, 2005), with psychological and social factors often seen as optional add-ons and sometimes scarcely mentioned at all. As a result, it is more of a 'bio-bio-bio model' in practice (Sharfstein, 2005).

There are similar problems with the highly influential and popular vulnerability-stress theory. According to this model, 'mental disorders' result from interactions between vulnerabilities people already have and current life events or stresses. This sounds reasonable, except that these 'vulnerabilities' have come to be seen as mainly biological or genetic, such as hypothesised chemical imbalances in people's brains and inherited factors (Boyle, 2002b, 2011). As we've seen, these claims are not based on evidence. Another problem is that, instead of focusing attention on what has happened, vulnerability-stress theory often works the other way. For example, researchers spend far more time and money trying to find these supposed inner vulnerabilities than trying to understand 'what's happened' in people's lives (Read, 2010).

The outcome of this mixture of vulnerabilities and stresses is also still seen as an 'illness', in much the same way as infections that result from a weak immune system. This woman was encouraged to see her problems in this way by mental health services:

> I'd got the issue of [child sexual] abuse to deal with… I thought well maybe that caused [my bipolar disorder]… I mean I understand now that [abuse] can actually be a trigger but it's actually a trigger for something that's already there. (Leeming et al., 2009, p.15)

The implied message from services seems to be, 'Being sexually abused as a child must have been very difficult for you, but it's not enough to explain your distress. You already had a tendency to develop bipolar disorder and the sexual abuse probably triggered it.'

So, by locating the 'real' problem in their biology, both the biopsychosocial and vulnerability-stress models can discourage us from looking too closely at what has happened, what it meant to the person, and how these 'stresses' came to be part of their life. Yet, if we look again at the circumstances and events most strongly linked with many forms of distress and troubling behaviour, a very different picture emerges. All the factors we listed at the beginning of the chapter involve inequalities of power – between men and women, White people and Black people, rich and poor, adults and children, employers and employees and states/governments and their citizens. These inequalities are known to be relevant to distress. And there is no evidence that the life experiences associated with inequalities are simply 'triggers' for biological vulnerabilities that we haven't yet found. Or that the outcomes are diagnosable illnesses. Yet direct discussions of power are more or less absent from psychiatric, psychological or psychotherapeutic theories and media discussions of why people become distressed.

The PTMF sees these power inequalities as central to understanding emotional and psychological distress and being able to offer constructive help. Power is also a key factor in linking these difficulties to wider social processes and highlighting the need for social action and social justice. This is a very different approach from conventional biopsychosocial or vulnerability-stress models.

In the next sections, we outline some general points about power and then describe its role in the PTMF.

Power is everywhere

What is power and why is it so important? There is no one definition because power refers to a complex set of processes, abstract and concrete, more and less visible. Here are three suggested definitions. Power is:

- being able to obtain security and advantages for yourself or others
- being able to influence your environment to meet your own needs and interests
- controlling resources that other people want, need or fear (Robertson, 2013; Smail, 2005).

It is hard to convey the complexity and impact of power in a single definition, especially as it often operates below our awareness and without our conscious intention. Michel Foucault, a French philosopher and social theorist, has been very influential in informing how we think about the less obvious aspects of power and how these relate to our feelings and behaviour. Foucault challenged traditional ideas that saw power mainly as something very evident that is 'possessed' by particular individuals or groups or located in specific places. This kind of power does exist, but Foucault argued that, in modern, more liberal democratic societies, other less easily recognised forms of power have become increasingly important. He was interested in the ways power actually operates in our everyday lives, as part of every organisation, social relationship or interaction, whether acknowledged or not.

Above all, Foucault focused on the ways power can produce or create social norms and standards, identities, desires and knowledge. Examples would be the desire to be thin, or to be a 'real man', or to own certain possessions. The *DSM*'s role in defining a huge range of behaviour and feelings as 'symptoms' and in producing new identities via forms of 'mental disorder' is also an example of this process.

Language and the idea of *discourse* are very important in this way of thinking about power. 'Discourse' refers to sets of related terms or images we use when representing, talking or writing about particular groups or phenomena. People who study discourse look for patterns in how we talk or write about ourselves and the wider world, and at their social and psychological effects. This echoes the African-American writer Toni Morrison's description of language as 'an act – with consequences' (1993).

These consequences are far reaching. Discourses can create positive and negative identities or make it look as if some people deserve power and privilege more than others. They can make some experiences or social contributions invisible and some more visible and valued. They can make some claims seem like facts and hide their cultural roots. They can make some courses of action seem reasonable and justified and others seem unreasonable or even unthinkable. We describe this in more detail later, when we discuss ideological power, but these are some brief examples:

▫ People who don't take psychiatric or other drugs prescribed for them are often said to be 'non-compliant' or 'non-adherent'. This suggests they are unreliable or disobedient, won't look after themselves or can't stick with things. It makes it more difficult to have an open conversation with professionals about why we might choose not to take prescribed drugs or find it hard to follow a drug regime. And it supports efforts to 'ensure compliance'.

▫ 'Work' is usually defined as paid employment – this is what comes to mind when we talk about 'going to work' or 'being out of work' or when we ask someone 'what work do you do?' This means that a huge amount of work that people – often those from disadvantaged groups – have to do becomes invisible or devalued. It includes housework, caring for children or other dependants, maintaining an acceptable feminine appearance, looking after a family's emotional needs, constantly smiling at customers, looking for paid employment, or preparing for welfare interviews and assessments.

▫ Militaristic language is often used in relation to illness. We talk about 'fighting disease' and 'losing the battle against cancer', and about certain treatments as 'magic bullets'. This puts us in opposition with our own bodies. It can make it difficult to refuse treatment (for fear of seeming like a coward) or to talk about being frightened or just accepting of illness, and it encourages us to see death as defeat and failure.

It is the effects of language and discourse that make them so important when thinking about power, especially the less obvious forms of power that affect all of us in our everyday lives. But more visible forms of power also have an impact and the two are closely connected. Together, they operate through both immediate and more distant processes – through our bodies and relationships and through social structures, institutions, organisations and everyday interactions. They operate with and without our conscious awareness.

In the PTMF, we have suggested a way of grouping various forms of power that are potentially relevant to many forms of distress and troubling behaviour. These are as follows.

Biological or embodied power

This is about our bodies and physical characteristics. For example, we might have good health, an attractive physical appearance, fertility, sporting talent and so on. Or we might experience physical limitations such as pain, disease, brain injury, disfigurement and disability. Biological power is also about the cultural meanings of our bodily characteristics and how our society accommodates and caters for them. This includes the meanings of attributes such as body shape and size or skin shade and colour, which can strongly affect our day-to-day experience. It also includes how far our physical environment is 'disability friendly'.

Interpersonal power

All forms of power can operate through relationships, but this refers more specifically to the power to look after/not look after, support or protect someone, to abandon or leave them, and to give/withdraw/withhold love or praise. Our relationships are vital sources of security, support, protection, validation, love and connection, which means that how interpersonal power operates in our lives, especially in childhood, can have profound effects on our sense of who we are and how we deal with life's difficulties.

Coercive power or power by force

This kind of power involves using violence, aggression, threats, physical strength, certain gestures and postures or reminders of past violence to frighten and intimidate someone, make them do things they don't want to or prevent them doing what they want. Although it is often negative, coercive power can be used positively – for example, when parents remove young children from danger. Negative coercive power is always part of child physical and sexual abuse, bullying, domestic violence and abuse, sexual assault and rape.

Legal power

This can also involve coercion, such as police powers to stop and search, arrest and imprison. The law can also protect our rights and support or limit other forms of power. It may prosecute and restrict the freedom of people who cause harm, or it may fail to accord equal rights to certain people or groups or to prosecute someone who has harmed others. Many government policies, such as those on welfare, housing and education, are backed by legal powers to ensure people get the benefits and services they are entitled to. However, the law can also be used to impose unfair or harmful policies. Legal powers are used to enforce some mental health practices, such as compulsory hospitalisation and physical interventions, and these can also be experienced as damaging.

Economic and material power

This is about the ability to obtain goods and services necessary for our wellbeing, to meet financial demands and take part in valued activities. Economic power allows us to secure food, housing, employment, transport, education, medical treatment, safety and security, physical space and privacy and to access legal services and leisure, sport and cultural activities. Economic power can also mean being able to control other people's access to these possessions or services – for example, as an employer or landlord or as the person who manages the household finances. As well as this, welfare systems and wider social and economic policies and structures can have a huge influence on economic power across individuals and society. People with access to economic power can also influence these policies to their own advantage.

Social/cultural capital

This is about having access to valued educational and job opportunities, qualifications, knowledge, shared experience and connections that ease people's way through life and confer a sense of social confidence and belonging. All of these benefits can be passed indirectly to the next generation. Without social capital, we can struggle to find helpful information to deal with difficult life situations or pursue our rights. We can also feel excluded from, uncomfortable in, or undeserving of various forms of influence and opportunities, such as high status jobs, cultural activities, education or healthcare.

Ideological power

This involves control of meaning, language, discourse and 'agendas'. It is one of the least visible but most important forms of power, because it is about our thoughts and beliefs, how we ought to think and feel, how we see ourselves, others and the wider world and what we take as 'natural' or 'facts'. It is about the effects of language and discourse, as we saw in the examples we gave earlier.

Ideological power can operate to:

- hold back certain issues or groups from public scrutiny
- bring people to see their interests and wants in particular ways
- create certain kinds of 'factual' knowledge about our thoughts, feelings, and behaviour
- reframe social problems as individual dysfunctions
- create beliefs or stereotypes about particular groups
- support some actions or policies over others
- allow you to interpret your own or others' experience, behaviour and feelings and have these meanings accepted by others, or
- silence or undermine.

Linking power, distress and troubling behaviour

The forms of power we've listed are very closely connected and often reinforce each other. Ideological power, especially, is part of every other form of power. This, and the fact that power operates in very varied ways and that there are many other factors involved, means it is rarely possible to say that *this* form of power will have *that* outcome.

Seeing how power might be operating in our lives is not always easy. Clinical psychologist David Smail suggests that we all live within a restricted 'power horizon' that makes it difficult for us to identify the less obvious or more distant reasons for what is happening in our lives here and now. Some of these limitations are probably unavoidable. As Smail points out:

> So many of our joys and frustrations, loves and hatreds arise from our contact with those immediately around us, that we can easily forget that there is a world beyond them… an infinitely wider field of power relations of which [we] need have no awareness. (Smail, 2005, pp.29–30)

Those who benefit from current systems of power are also often keen to hide its operation, and ideological power plays an important part here. Our restricted power horizon not only limits our understanding of our own and others' feelings and behaviour; it also provides opportunities for 'the more or less deliberate exploitation of our perspective' (Smail, 2005, p.33). The PTMF aims to broaden our power horizon, to encourage what Smail calls 'outsight', so as better to understand our own and others' distress and troubling behaviour and find constructive ways forward.

In a general sense, power can create and maintain distress by producing very difficult and challenging circumstances that pose a range of psychological, social and physical threats. However, because ideological power is so often hidden and unacknowledged, we will first give some examples of processes where it plays a major role in encouraging us to see our feelings and behaviour in certain ways, and in promoting or undermining certain meanings in our daily lives.

Before we discuss this, it's important to note that a major source of ideological and many other forms of power in any society is its dominant economic system and the assumptions on which it is based. In many Western (especially the US and the UK) and some non-Western societies, this economic system has, since about the 1980s, been 'neoliberalism'. In Box 1 (over page), we describe some far-reaching social and psychological effects of this economic philosophy. It might be helpful to read the following examples of ideological power, especially the first two, in conjunction with Box 1.

Ideological power 1: Cultural narratives of distress

Every society has its own ways of interpreting people's feelings and behaviour, especially those that are distressing, disturbing, unusual or extreme. We learn these 'narratives of distress' directly and indirectly: for example, through our relationships, through storylines in books, film and theatre and on TV, and through websites, magazines and newspapers. However, some ways of talking about and representing distress are much more common than others. In modern Western societies, as we've seen, by far the most dominant narrative is one that likens troubling emotions and behaviour to medical illnesses that are caused primarily by abnormal biological processes and probably require treatment with drugs.

Box 1 – Neoliberalism

The term 'neoliberalism' is a shorthand description for the economic system that has been influential in many Western societies since the 1980s. It is based on the work of economists such as Friedrich Hayek, Milton Friedman and the Chicago School. Its ideas were initially applied in the UK by governments led by Margaret Thatcher and in the US by Ronald Reagan.

Neoliberalism emphasises individual freedom, autonomy, choice, self-sufficiency and responsibility and promotes the idea that businesses should be as free from rules and regulations as possible. This is said to be necessary for efficiency and prosperity. These ideas have supported minimising the role of the state by policies such as reducing spending on welfare and public services. Since the 1980s, many state assets, such as public transport and parts of the NHS, have been privatised. The introduction of flexible or zero hours contracts and moves to 'self-employment' have led to many jobs becoming insecure. Competition is encouraged through targets, league tables and rankings in many areas of life, from factory work to health and education.

Like all economic systems, neoliberalism gains much of its power from encouraging people to believe certain things about themselves and others that make them more likely to co-operate with rather than challenge the system. For example:

- People are seen, and encouraged to see themselves, as competitive and self-reliant rather than interdependent and interlinked.

- Our most important roles are seen as being workers and consumers contributing to economic profit. Other roles, such as partners, parents, volunteers or carers are secondary to our availability for work.

- Our status and worth is measured mainly by economic power, such as our ability to spend money on material goods and services. People who do not achieve highly in these ways may be devalued and devalue themselves – for example, as 'unskilled workers'. Those who claim welfare payments may be seen as 'scroungers' or 'work-shy'.

- This is reinforced by claims that success depends on our personal qualities, such as aspiration, character, resilience and so on.

Neoliberal policies are associated with emotional distress in many ways, including:

- They create insecurity in many areas of our lives such as work, income, housing, community ties, relationships, status and physical wellbeing.

- People are kept in an almost constant state of dissatisfaction about their lives, possessions, achievements, bodies and relationships, and then persuaded to buy solutions. Neoliberalism is associated with increases in the gap between the richest and poorest people in society, which encourages this kind of social comparison. However, these solutions – the latest gadgets or fashions or the most expensive holidays and so on – do not address the real underlying social and financial insecurities in our lives.

- Individuals are then encouraged to blame themselves for their failure to meet the standards being promoted. Psychology and psychiatry play a major role here by suggesting that the causes of distress lie in our personality characteristics, psychological dysfunctions and 'mental illnesses' or 'disorders'. This, in turn, disconnects these problems from social and economic policies and helps preserve the status quo.

- Solutions to distress – drugs and most therapies – are also aimed at individuals rather than society. Increasingly, recovery is defined in terms of making people 'economically active' again – in other words, returning them to work, however poorly paid or stressful their jobs are. The Welfare to Work and Improving Access to Psychological Therapy (IAPT) programmes are examples of this kind of solution. These programmes can be very profitable for the providers, although outcomes may be poor.

All of this maintains cycles in which the economic system profits through creating distress and in then offering ways of understanding and solving it (see Barber, 2007; Bender, 2019; Friedli & Stearn, 2015; Moncrieff, 2008b; Verhaeghe, 2014; Wilkinson & Pickett, 2018).

Medical narratives are already very powerful in our society, partly because they draw on the wider narratives and language of science and its associations with progress, breakthroughs, discoveries, experiments, facts and statistics. This combination creates ways of speaking that have considerable ideological power and can be especially difficult to question.

Other forms of power are also important here. For example, pharmaceutical companies spend very large amounts of money supporting medical narratives of distress. They do this through advertising and marketing, direct contact with prescribers such as GPs to persuade them of the benefits of new medications, sponsoring conferences, ghost-writing research articles, funding professionals and researchers, including those who devise diagnostic manuals, and supporting charity and professional campaigning and celebrity endorsements. Pharmaceutical companies also research people's hopes, fears and discontents and use these to guide how they promote their products (Cosgrove & Wheeler, 2013; Goldacre, 2012).

The media is an important source of narratives of distress. Medical narratives are the default way of talking about distress in TV and radio programmes and in newspaper reports and feature articles, using the unquestioned language of 'symptoms', 'illness' and 'disorders'. Reports of 'breakthroughs' in biological research into causes or treatments are often presented uncritically. When these breakthroughs come to nothing, it is very rarely given the same publicity (Harper, 2020; Joseph, 2015, 2020; Morrill, 2019). Reports about areas of debate or disagreement are much harder to find and still tend to be framed within a medical perspective, for example questions about overprescribing, misdiagnosis or lack of funding for services. These stories tell us very little about debates in mental health or what non-medical alternatives there are (Henderson, 2019; Leo & Lacasse, 2008). For all these reasons, readers of this book may not have had the chance to hear about dissenting or non-medical views about distress.

Unfortunately, the only alternative discourse that is on offer is the one we've called the 'brain or blame' dilemma. There seems to be a widespread assumption that either someone's brain is faulty or else they or their relatives must be responsible, perhaps through bad parenting or psychological weakness (Boyle, 2013).

For example, diagnoses of 'schizophrenia' have been defended on the grounds that, without it, 'the person, rather than the illness' would be 'blamed for the symptoms' (Lieberman & First, 2007). Given these two stark alternatives, it can seem as if the medical narrative is the more scientific, non-judgemental option. It also suggests that 'blame or brain' are the only possible choices. We will return to this in the next section.

Reflecting on all this, clinical psychologist Dave Harper comments that:

> ... the public conversation [about narratives of distress] is not a level playing field since some narratives are promoted by institutions with societal power and significant financial resources. (Harper, 2020)

Why is this so important? Partly because the unequal public conversation about distress limits the ways in which we can understand and respond to our problems. As feminist scholar and activist Jill Johnston puts it, you can only say what you are 'according to what they say you can be' (1974, p.68). Philosopher Miranda Fricker (2007) has coined the useful term 'epistemic injustice' to encompass the situation where people – often members of disadvantaged groups – are deprived of the necessary resources (such as information, ideas, contacts and confidence) to understand their experiences differently from the dominant mainstream perspectives. All of this can limit our options for change.

Laura Delano was told she had 'bipolar disorder'. She says:

> [I] became a full-blooded patient, passive and dependent and convinced of her brokenness, in a matter of weeks. I believed [doctor] when he said I'd need 'meds' for the rest of my life, and would have to learn how to 'manage my symptoms' and 'set realistic expectations' for myself... (Delano, 2013)

She goes on to describe how she came to see her situation in a different way when she came across Robert Whitaker's book, *Anatomy of an Epidemic* (2011):

> ... I couldn't have predicted in my wildest imaginings that the result would be an awakening... [But]... something

inside of me was desperate for change… and all it took was an openness, and a readiness to try out a different way of thinking. It was a way of thinking that required I leave behind every single belief I held about myself – that I was 'mentally ill', that I had a 'chemical imbalance', and that I needed 'medication' to 'treat' this 'condition' that made me eternally different.

Not everyone will experience such a vivid 'awakening'. But encountering new ways of thinking, new narratives that change the balance of ideological power, can be transformative.

Ideological power 2: Self-surveillance and self-policing

As well as guiding our interpretations of our own and others' distress, cultural narratives also tell us about norms, values, standards and expectations in almost every area of our lives. This includes acceptable and unacceptable feelings and behaviour about gender roles; our appearance; how to talk about and display feelings; how to bring up children; what we should want to achieve; what 'success' means, and so on. This is what Foucault meant by the creative qualities of power.

In large, complex societies, different groups will have different standards and expectations, but there is also increasing uniformity. Advertising, branding, the media and, of course, social media have a major role in this. Diagnostic manuals also play an important part, telling us not just what is normal and abnormal but that these standards have the backing of science, making them less easy to question. As we described in Chapter 2, sociologist Bruce Cohen has shown that each edition of the *DSM* adds more criteria about what counts as unacceptable or 'abnormal' behaviour in schools and workplaces. He links this to modern neoliberal demands for a compliant and productive workforce (Cohen, 2016; see also Timimi, 2011).

We are all exposed to these influences. And it starts early. Talking about gender norms and the 'all but impossible task' of raising children in a non-sexist way in Western society, the psychologist Cordelia Fine (2011, p.238) comments: 'How should children ignore gender when they continually watch it, hear it, see it; are clothed in it, sleep in it, eat off it?' The ever-present quality of these and other 'should and ought' messages is part of their influence.

Less easy to identify but just as important is what is sometimes called self-surveillance and self-policing. This doesn't just mean being very aware of ourselves and how we behave. It means adopting the point of view of another person or group – sometimes known as an 'other' – who represents the current cultural standards and expectations about behaviour, personal characteristics, desires and achievements. We then monitor ourselves and 'police' our own feelings and behaviour in line with these standards. However, we don't always realise we are doing this, especially when standards and expectations are very much taken for granted.

In earlier Christian societies, this 'other' could have been an all-seeing God who was believed to be keeping an eye on our sinful behaviour. Feminists have written about 'the male gaze', where girls and women are socialised to see themselves through men's eyes and adjust their appearance and behaviour to please, or not displease, men. In one way or another, people in less powerful groups, because of their age, class, ethnicity, sexuality or ability, are likely to find themselves 'policing' their behaviour in line with the dominant group's perspective (Eddo-Lodge, 2018; O'Grady, 2005). Societies that place a strong emphasis on individual identities rather than on the family, tribe or community encourage all of us to meet idealised standards through competition and material possessions, and to take a great deal of personal responsibility for doing so. There is often a strong emphasis on our 'freedom to choose'. This makes it all the more difficult to identify the 'other' whose standards we are expected to meet, or the sources of power that are operating behind the scenes. It is not surprising that people often claim 'I'm doing it for myself' or 'It's my choice' and feel intense personal failure if they do not achieve their aims.

Of course, the pressure to engage in a constant process of improvement of ourselves and our relationships, possessions, appearance and achievements, in comparison with other people and to the benefit of business profits, is not new. However, it has greatly increased under neoliberalism and has been encouraged by social media,[5] which the journalist Yomi Adegoke (2020) has described

---

5. In 2019, Facebook and Instagram conducted trials where people could not see the…

as 'an invisible scoreboard looming in the sky'. Sometimes the scoreboard is very visible, when we are provided with tools to monitor and measure our activities and bodily functioning and even our mental health (Simons, 2020). At the same time, our limited power to control important aspects of our lives is hidden by discourses of personal choice and the need to possess individual qualities such as aspiration, self-control, strength of character or resilience. All of this means that our 'power horizon' can be very restricted.

Even more confusingly, the ideal standards we are urged to meet are often contradictory. We are told we should eat healthy foods and stay within the approved weight range but not become so focused on food that we develop an 'eating disorder'. Parents should be emotionally present for their children, but not to the extreme of being overprotective or 'helicopter parents' who monitor their children too much. Children must achieve high grades in order to be successful but shouldn't get too stressed about exams. We should put a great deal of work into our appearance, take exercise, go to the gym, use beauty treatments and even cosmetic surgery, but not develop 'body dysmorphic disorder', and so on. The singer Taylor Swift has talked about contradictory standards around women's bodies, in relation to her eating problems (Snapes, 2020):

> There's always some standard of beauty that you're not meeting. Because if you're thin enough, then you don't have that ass that everybody wants, but if you have enough weight on you to have an ass, then your stomach isn't flat enough. It's all just fucking impossible.

If we fail to meet these and other standards, we can see ourselves – and fear we are seen by others – as inadequate, deficient or even pathological. Self-criticism, self-blame, self-silencing and shame are common responses.[6]

... number of 'likes' their friends' posts were given, reducing opportunities for social comparison. A spokeswoman said that the change was 'based on wellbeing research and feedback from mental health professionals on the effect of comparing likes' (Australian Associated Press, 2019).

6. See Chapter 4 of the main PTMF document, especially the sections on gender and social class and poverty.

Sometimes, self-surveillance and social comparison are so exhausting and distressing that they contribute to being given a psychiatric diagnosis. These quotes from new mothers and fathers diagnosed as having 'depression' show the pressure to live up to standards at a stage in life that is full of messages about how people ought to feel and behave:

> One of the reasons I felt so down was because I had to admit to myself that I was not an earth mother... and my feeling deep down was that I was failing as a mother if I couldn't cope with being at home. (Mauthner, 2010, p.470)

> I lie to my health visitor. I lie to my friends. I lie to myself. I post happy pictures online. I want to look like a capable person, a successful feminist, having it all her way. But I am breaking myself. (Unsworth, 2019)

> ... there was a great deal of shame, too – at my frailty, my uselessness as a father, my inability to 'man up' and face the challenges of caring for my son. (Swami, 2019)

These quotes also show why the 'brain' pole of the 'brain or blame' alternatives can be so attractive. The implied message is, 'You have failed to manage as well as other people do, but this is because there is something wrong with your brain and not because you are a weak or inadequate person.' But this sense of relief from guilt comes at the cost of taking on another negative identity, that of someone who is 'mentally ill'. This has been described as the 'diagnosis as salvation and damnation' dilemma (Leeming et al., 2009). The PTMF offers a way out of this dilemma by shifting surveillance away from us, as individuals, and towards the potentially harmful cultural standards and the power processes that drive them in so many areas of our lives. This also helps us understand why people who have not suffered obvious trauma can still experience significant emotional distress.

Ideological power 3: Invalidation

Invalidation refers to the process of having your point of view, your experience or the sense you make of it ignored, dismissed, trivialised or silenced. In general, the power to invalidate not just individuals but entire groups is more likely to be held by adults, men, White people, the able-bodied, heterosexuals, wealthy and educated people and those generally agreed by society to be sane. These people are over-represented in the higher ranks of organisations, government and other places of influence. We can see how this form of ideological power interacts with other forms of power, such as legal, biological and economic, and with social and cultural capital. Invalidation is especially important in protecting more powerful groups from scrutiny. It is another aspect of Miranda Fricker's 'epistemic injustice', where the views or experiences of some individuals or groups are routinely given less credibility or status.

Invalidation is sometimes visible or noticeable only when something is absent. For example, Western accounts of historical or recent events, including what is taught in schools and colleges, are often those of White men. Accounts by, say, women or non-Western groups may be presented as a 'special' perspective, leaving other accounts simply as 'history' or 'reporting'. We will see in Chapter 10 how the perspective of people with psychiatric diagnoses has been seen as a less important source of evidence in research on troubling emotions and behaviour. We also saw, in the section on cultural narratives of distress above, that non-medicalised accounts are routinely overlooked.

People from minority and other disadvantaged groups also say that they rarely see people like them and their experiences or perspectives portrayed in the media, except in stereotypical roles:

> I am a gay female and I often feel as though the media only seems to have one specific idea of what a female is/wants/ desires. I often feel alienated and unseen/unacknowledged. (Bates, 2014, p.289)

Another form of invalidation occurs when those from less powerful groups are assumed to be inferior in some way, or stereotyped into certain roles, as happened to Dawn Butler, a Black female member of the UK Parliament:

> I was in the [Members] lift and some other [White male] MP said 'This lift really isn't for cleaners'. (BBC News, 2016)

Links between invalidation and control of meaning are very obvious when sexual, racial and other insults or harassment are dismissed by perpetrators as 'joking' or 'just banter', or when people from advantaged groups deny that a problem exists. Reni Eddo-Lodge wrote her book *Why I'm No Longer Talking to White People About Race* (2018) as a response to such experiences of denial and as a way of '[articulating] that feeling of having your voice and confidence snatched away from you in the cocky face of the status quo' (p.xvii).

Invalidation is a common aspect of the coercive power involved in child sexual abuse, rape, sexual assault and domestic violence, when the perpetrator imposes a particular version of reality on the victim: for example, that they 'asked for it', enjoyed it or even that it did not happen. Invalidation also happens in mental health services. Unwanted medical meanings may be backed by legal power and forced physical interventions. Invalidation can also be more routine, as some of the service-user consultants to the PTMF project described:

> … absolutely everything I had to say, including that the drugs were making things worse, [staff] made me, and more specifically my brain, the problem, rather than my traumatic experiences.

> Meaning to what was going on was given by medics to my detriment and [any resistance] resulted in being labelled as a troublemaker. As a direct consequence, I started not being able to trust people. (Johnstone & Boyle, 2018a, Chapter 7)

One reason these systematic forms of invalidation are so powerful is that they draw on wider cultural meanings that reinforce the more dominant group's/person's perspective, as we discuss further in Chapter 10. This includes assumptions such as seeing Western worldviews as more scientifically informed or seeing women as more emotional and less rational than men. Similarly, children and people with learning disabilities or mental health problems may be seen as less believable when they talk about their experiences, to the point where criminal proceedings for assaults against them may be dropped (Kelly et al., 2005; Stanko et al., 2007). The term 'false memory syndrome' combines some of these stereotypes. It suggests that alleged victims of childhood sexual abuse might be suffering from a disorder in which they believe things that did not happen. Eddo-Lodge (2018) talks about the White stereotype of 'angry Black people' that can silence those facing racial harassment or discrimination.

Invalidation also draws on popular beliefs about how people should behave in certain situations, such as: 'Why didn't you just speak up/tell them what you thought/report it/ignore it/fight back/ just leave after he hit you?' Questions like these ignore the power dynamics involved and make less powerful groups responsible for changing the situation. Natalie Collins works with women who have been abused by their male partners, and comments that, when people hear what she does, they often ask, 'Why doesn't she just leave?' but that no one has ever asked, 'Why doesn't he just stop?' (Collins, 2019, p.39).

All of this means that invalidation can be repeated and reinforced in legal, welfare and mental health services and by colleagues, friends and family (Salter, 2012):

> My partner… was able to persuade both me and those around me that I was mad, that I lacked insight, and that my worries (including about him) were manifestations of my 'paranoid delusions'.… My partner positioned himself as my carer and my friends would often tell me that, considering my 'condition', I should be grateful to have someone around so dedicated to my well-being. That condition was never doubted by anyone. My partner escorted me to psychiatric appointments, where the professionals listened sympathetically to him, valuing his sane perspective. (Carr, 2020)

More generally, invalidation can lead to lack of confidence in your own views; anxiety about speaking in public; feeling isolated; difficulties in understanding your own feelings and experience; self-doubt, self-silencing and self-blame (Am I oversensitive? Should I have said something? Was it all my fault? Did that really happen?). People can be reluctant to report even criminal acts because they might not be believed. And if your views and experiences are not validated, or are subtly or forcefully invalidated, then it can also be difficult to give a clear account of them, reinforcing doubts about the worth of your perspective.

....

We have now explored in detail the many ways in which ideological power reinforces other forms of power, such as legal, embodied and economic/material. We will return to these issues in Chapter 6 on 'Meaning'. First, in Chapter 5, we will take a closer look at how the negative operation of power can affect people by creating threats in all aspects of their lives.

Exercise 3

'What has happened to you?' (How is power operating in your life?)

Think about how the seven types of power outlined on pages 43–46 apply in your life, or the life of the person you are working with/supporting.

If you choose to work through all the exercises, you will find that the questions and responses overlap, so that by thinking about the role of power in your life, you will inevitably be thinking about threats and meanings and, perhaps, threat responses as well. Don't get held up by wondering which response belongs under which heading, because the questions are simply different angles on the same experiences. You may want to use the template on page 91 of the online guided discussion (at **www.bps.org.uk/sites/www. bps.org.uk/files/Policy/Policy%20-%20Files/PTM%20Guided%20 Discussion.pdf**) so that you can jot down ideas as you go along in whatever order they occur to you and under whatever heading makes most sense – or perhaps under several headings.

If this exercise is in any way difficult or upsetting, take a break and use the ideas and resources from Exercise 2 in the previous chapter.

Chapter 5
'How did what happened affect you?' (What kind of threats does this pose?)

When power operates negatively, against our interests, it can create very aversive and challenging circumstances in our lives. We know a lot about this through research on the kinds of environments where individuals, families, communities and whole societies do well or struggle. This research also tells us about the conditions that are needed in order for humans to maintain their wellbeing. We've called these our 'core needs'. There isn't a definitive list, but they include:

- to be safe, valued and cared for in our earliest relationships with caregivers

- to have a sense of security and belonging in a family/friendship/social group

- to feel safe and secure in our physical environment

- to form intimate relationships and partnerships

- to experience and manage a range of emotions

- to feel valued and effective in our family/social roles

- to have some control over important parts of our lives, including our bodies and emotions

- to meet basic physical and material needs for ourselves and our dependants

- to experience some sense of justice or fairness about our circumstances
- to have connections to the natural world
- to engage in meaningful activities and, more generally, to have a sense of hope, meaning and purpose in our lives.

We summarised research for these in Chapter 4, and you can find and read more in Chapter 4 of the full PTMF report, and elsewhere (for example, Hari, 2018; Jetten et al., 2012; Tay & Diener, 2011; WHO, 2002).

How each of us tries to meet these needs and the importance we give to any one of them will vary a great deal between different people, times and places. However, in the PTMF we argue that anything that prevents these core needs being met, in whatever way, may be experienced as a threat to emotional, physical, relational and/or social safety and survival. We also argue that humans have evolved to be able to draw on a range of threat responses that help to protect us from core threats and that support our psychological, social and physical survival. In other words, these threat responses are attempts to meet our core needs under very difficult circumstances. In mental health services, many of these threat responses are labelled as psychiatric symptoms. We discuss threat responses in Chapter 7, under the question, 'What did you have to do to survive?'

Core threats, needs and power

We can see core threats to safety, survival or wellbeing as the opposite or reverse of core human needs. These threats create aversive life circumstances where we are likely to struggle rather than flourish. Core threats can occur in these areas:

Within relationships – for example, with parents, carers, partners, other relatives, friends, colleagues, teachers, healthcare professionals and other important people in our lives. Threats to these relationships include being abandoned, rejected by or losing people you love, care for or depend on; being undermined or invalidated through criticism, humiliation, having your feelings and beliefs dismissed or having other people's views or meanings imposed on you, even if you don't agree; lack of love, care and protection; emotional, physical or material neglect; sexual, physical or emotional abuse; receiving confusing communications; being bullied; experiencing domestic violence; intergenerational trauma that is passed down through parents and other relatives.

Bodily – for example, ill health, chronic pain, bodily disability, injury, loss of function, physical danger, starvation, exhaustion, physical attacks and invasion through sexual assault, and other forms of violence and coercion.

Emotional – when faced with threats, people can feel out of control, overwhelmed by feelings that are very hard to manage.

Economic/material – for example, threats to financial security or housing; not being able to meet basic physical or material needs or access basic services for yourself and/or dependants; not being able to share social activities, give presents, repair or replace things that have broken; struggling with chronic debt.

Social/community – for example, isolation, exclusion, hostility at work or in your neighbourhood; being unable to compete in achievement, status and so forth; injustice/unfairness, loss of social or work role.

Environmental – for example, lack of safety; living in substandard housing; living in a dense, urban or high-crime area; loss of connection with the natural world; loss of connection with your homeland.

Knowledge and meaning construction – for example, lack of opportunity, support or social resources to find out about and use important sources of information to make sense of your experiences; devaluing by others of your own knowledge, understandings and experiences; imposition of meanings by social discourses and more powerful others, including in mental health services.

Identity – for example, lack of support to develop your own identity; loss of status; loss of social, cultural or religious identity, such as being a worker, a parent or a member of a particular social or ethnic group. We may be given messages that we or the social group we identify with are inferior or something to be ashamed of through day-to-day discrimination or abuse or through the media, government policies and other influential external forces.

Value base – for example, loss of purpose, values, beliefs and meanings; loss of community rituals, beliefs and practices. These threats are common for refugees and people seeking asylum, but they also happen if, for example, people derive no sense of meaning from their work or they can't express their values through it.

What makes threats easier or harder to survive?

A large part of the negative impact of these threats comes from factors that reinforce or make them worse. These factors aren't threats in themselves but are aspects of threatening situations, such as:

- the threats happen during childhood
- there is no one to support you, confide in or offer protection
- there are many kinds of threat
- the threats are long lasting, repeated and/or severe
- there is no clear way to avoid or escape the threatening situation ('entrapment')
- it is not possible/easy to predict when the threats will happen or to control them when they do
- the threats involve your sense of self or your worth as a person
- the threats happen within a close emotional relationship with someone you love and depend on
- the threats are intentional, directed specifically at you
- the threat(s) come from several sources.

Not all of these reinforcing factors, and perhaps none, will be part of any particular threatening situation. However, adversities do often involve more than one type of threat. Losing your job can lead to economic and material, social and community threats, as well as threats to identity and relationships. Domestic violence and child abuse obviously involve threats to the body but also complex emotional and relational threats and entrapment. Being a refugee or asylum seeker can expose you to almost every type of threat.

Experiencing one kind of adversity also makes it more likely that you will experience others – adversities tend to be 'event producing situations' (Newton, 2013) – that is, one aversive situation can generate many more. For example, economic threats (poverty) can transform into major difficulties and situations we might otherwise easily manage, such as a short period of illness or the car breaking down. Threats experienced in childhood can have very long-lasting effects. This is because they limit vital opportunities for learning how to meet our core needs and for developing skills and supportive relationships that prepare us to deal with difficulties later in life.

All of this helps explain why events that look 'the same' can have very different impacts – a point we will return to. And all these aspects of difficult situations can, if reversed, help to support and protect us and lessen the long-term impact. For example, if a traumatic event happened when you were a bit older and was not repeated, and you were able to confide in a trusted adult and were believed, then it is more likely that you will be able to move on from it.

How does this relate to the operation of power? The PTMF sees many threats as arising from the negative operation of power, which is why the list of core threats partly maps onto the list of different forms of power in Chapter 4. But, because different forms of power and the threats they give rise to are so interrelated and are likely to be modified by the factors we've listed above, it is not possible to say that *this* form of power gives rise to *this* kind of threat. Below are some of the ways that power and threat interact.

□   One of the definitions of power we gave in the last chapter was 'being able to influence your environment to meet your own needs and interests'. Individuals and groups with greater access to power resources will be more able to meet their core needs and less likely to encounter threatening circumstances. So it is not surprising that the factors we listed at the beginning of Chapter 4 that are linked to troubling emotions and behaviour, such as child sexual and physical abuse, gender-based violence and racial discrimination, involve inequalities of power.

▫   What reduces threats for some people can increase them for others. In other words, some people or groups can meet their core needs in ways that are damaging to others. These damaging practices can be embedded in organisations or social institutions, including the family. Their potential for damage can also be hidden by ideological power – power over how we talk about and make sense of ourselves and the world. For example, the idea that some people should be able to accumulate large amounts of wealth has been justified by the claim that this wealth 'trickles down' to less advantaged people. Welfare policies that create multiple threats for many people are justified by language such as 'encouraging people into work' and calling unemployed people 'scroungers'. Abuses that happen within relationships can be written off as 'just a domestic' or given secondary importance to the institution of the 'nuclear family', gender role norms, personal privacy, parents' rights to discipline their children, and so on.

▫   Ideological power – supported by economic power – also encourages us to think in certain ways about our core needs and how they can be met. For example, as we've discussed, modern Western societies promote the idea that we should think about our identities, value, sense of belonging and purpose in terms of accumulating material possessions or having a certain appearance or educational achievements. Our highly individualistic culture also promotes the belief that we can meet many, if not all our core needs through our own efforts and inner resources – by 'self-management' or 'self-improvement'. All of this can result in feelings of failure or self-blame in the face of adversity (see Chapter 4).

▫   All kinds of threats to core needs are more common in contexts of inequality and other sorts of deprivation, discrimination, exclusion, marginalisation and social injustice. Looked at like this, it is not difficult to see why childhood adversities and poverty are such major causes of mental health problems; indeed, poverty is sometimes called 'the cause of the causes' of these problems.[1] Those who already lack ideological and/or embodied power in our society, such as very old people, some minority ethnic groups, women and

1. See the sections on childhood adversity and social class and poverty in Chapter 4 of the main PTMF document.

people with disabilities are also more likely to be poor. Moreover, we don't just have one identity or belong to one social group, and some of these several identities will reinforce powerlessness and some will lessen it (see, for example, Crenshaw, 1989; Johnstone & Boyle, 2018a, Chapter 6, pp.218–223). Lack of economic power adds to the threats these groups are already experiencing so that they may have little control over many important areas of life as well as experience threats to safety and security, relationships, and physical health:

> It sounds ridiculous, but three or four pounds can sometimes be the difference with getting evicted… and living in your property. (Quoted in Moffat et al., 2016, p.200)

And because money and material possessions are such important sources of status and identity in our society, their lack often threatens our social standing, leading to shame and humiliation. Ideological power obviously plays a part here, through the meanings attached to money and possessions but also, for example, through common meanings or discourses about gender roles and about the 'deserving' and 'undeserving' poor, as these examples show (Chase & Walker, 2012):

> The headmistress, she's got a little tick box and she's like, 'Well, she lives on [name] Road, that ticks her off as one bad parent; she's a single mother; she doesn't have a job. Well, we can clearly see that she's got emotional problems and she's struggling. Son's got behavioural problems'… so when I go to that meeting, she's there thinking, 'Oh my God, it's just another one of those mothers'.
> (A woman talking about a forthcoming meeting with the head of her son's primary school)

> I am the man in this relationship. I am meant to be the man… to take care of the missus and my kids. And I don't, and I hate feeling like I do with myself because of it. Sometimes there ain't no point in socialising. 'Cos what are you going to talk about? Your bills? Your debt? So, yes, that does make you withdraw I suppose… there's nothing to talk about except that you feel a bit depressed.

If you check my work record you can see that I haven't always claimed benefits... and I just thought 'If you checked that, you wouldn't make me feel so bad about sitting here'. (A woman talking about encounters with benefit advisers)

Money is also an essential resource for avoiding or escaping difficult circumstances, whether temporarily or permanently. It makes it more possible for us to have a night out, go on holiday, take time off work, move to a safer area, leave an abusive relationship, buy services from others and so on. In all these ways, lack of money creates entrapment and a build-up of threats and exacerbating factors. Children living in poverty are also affected by these threats, as well as by sexual and physical abuse, emotional neglect, family conflict and domestic violence. These adversities, which are found in all social groups, are even more entrapping for children because of the very large difference in power between them and adults.

▫   Unfortunately, power imbalances in mental health and other human systems can add to all this. For example, welfare systems routinely create economic threats through sanctions or maladministration. They can also create threats to identity by making people reveal a great deal of negative information about themselves and their circumstances. Mental health systems threaten people's ability to develop their own values and make meaning of their experience by imposing a medical explanation of their problems . This may lead to threats to the body through psychiatric drugs and other physical interventions.

▫   Sometimes, threats become so visible, severe and widespread they have to be 'officially' recognised. One effect of this is to widen our power horizon – in other words, make us aware of forms of power that are more distant and hidden. As more people talk and write about these threats, we become aware of distant sources of power we might otherwise not have known about but that can create very visible, immediate threats to our physical environment, safety and security, health and wellbeing, livelihoods, relationships and communities. Climate change is one example of this (Barnwell et al., 2020; Woodbury, 2019).

▫   Finally, it is important to remember that, in any context of power inequalities, there is always a threat to meaning-making through invalidation, where your point of view is overlooked, trivialised or dismissed (see Chapter 4).

Power is also positive

Because the PTMF is a way of understanding distress and troubling behaviour, it focuses more on the *negative* operation of power. But power also operates positively and, even in threatening circumstances, can offer ways of supporting and protecting us. Even disempowered individuals, groups, families and communities will have some access to sources of power that reduce the experience and impact of threat and help us meet our core needs in constructive ways. Positive sources of power can come from secure, protective early relationships and from current social support and feelings of belonging. Positive power also comes from having access to money, qualifications, knowledge and information about your situation that helps you manage or change it. We can also call on our physical abilities, such as strength and health, on our skills and talents and on the supportive relationships we might have with professionals or officials. Being able to join with others to share experiences and/or plan collective action to address threat and injustices, whether at local, national or global levels, is also a significant source of positive power. Writing about recovery from trauma and threat, Judith Herman notes that:

> Social action offers the survivor[s] a source of power that draws upon [their] own initiative, energy and resourcefulness but that magnifies these qualities far beyond [their] own capacities. It offers [them] an alliance with others based on cooperation and shared purpose. (Herman, 1992, p.207)

If you looked at Exercise 2 in Chapter 3, you'll have seen a longer list of these positive sources of power in relation to the question 'What are your strengths?'

We can see that, if we put together the many different ways power creates threats, plus the factors that may increase or reduce its impact and the positive power resources we can draw on, then no two people's experience of adversity will be exactly the same.

This is important in thinking about public stories of overcoming adversity. Some of these are helpful and inspirational. Others can give the impression that internal characteristics such as 'resilience', 'aspiration', 'persistence' or 'strength of character' are the central factors in overcoming adversity and achieving success in relationships, education and careers, recovery from mental health problems, social mobility and so on. These stories tend to downplay or overlook power inequalities and resources. As well as making some people feel like failures, this limits our understanding of how threat and adversity arise, why they persist and how we might, to some extent, be able to overcome them.

Perhaps one of the most important factors shaping our experience of threat and adversity is the meaning we make of it. We've already discussed meaning in relation to ideological power. We will return to it in more detail in the next chapter.

Exercise 4

'How did what happened affect you?' (What kind of threats does this pose?)

Like the previous exercise on power, this exercise may bring up difficult memories and situations. Please keep in mind the suggestions for looking after yourself outlined at the end of Chapter 3.

You can use the list at the beginning of this chapter to think about the threats you, or the person you are working with or supporting, have experienced. You may want to add them to the template on page 91 of the online guided discussion (at **www.bps. org.uk/sites/www.bps.org.uk/files/Policy/Policy%20-%20Files/ PTM%20Guided%20Discussion.pdf**). You will probably find you've already noted some of these when you were thinking about power, because the two are so interconnected.

You can then think about the list of factors that we have called 'What makes threats easier or harder to survive?' and make a list of those that are relevant to you, or jot them down on the template.

Chapter 6

'What sense did you make of it?' (What is the meaning of these situations and experiences to you?)

By now it will be clear that we cannot discuss any aspect of the PTMF core questions about power and threat (and in the next chapter, threat responses) without implying their meanings. As discussed in Chapter 2, the diagnostic model of distress sees people primarily as bodies that need fixing. In contrast, the PTMF sees human beings primarily as meaning-making creatures who actively try to make sense of their worlds. This starts from the moment of our birth. The main PTMF document (summarising the work of psychologists such as John Bowlby, Lev Vygotsky, Jerome Bruner and others) explains how babies learn to make distinctions between what is 'safe' and 'unsafe' and pleasurable and painful, and later, partly through language, absorb further meanings from their relationships with others. No one has a perfect upbringing, but many of us will be lucky enough to conclude, based on our very early relationships, that we are lovable and that others can be trusted. Others will have more difficult experiences that may lead them to conclude the opposite and to react accordingly. These meanings will profoundly shape our future lives and relationships.

Meanings shape our specific experiences as well as our general beliefs about the world. This is an obvious but crucial point. It implies that the same situation will be experienced very differently depending on the meaning it holds for us, which in turn will be shaped by the general power context. For example, having very little to eat will feel very different to someone who has chosen to go on a diet than it will to someone who has no money to buy food. Being on your own may be peaceful and relaxing if you are on a meditation retreat but may feel unbearable if you are an older person with no friends in your neighbourhood.

This chapter focuses on the role of the meanings we create about events or situations. A child who has been abused by a neighbour and who has been able to confide in a parent who believed, supported and comforted them, assured them it was not their fault and took steps to protect them has a good chance of coming to terms with this traumatic event without lasting damage. If, on the other hand, they had no one to confide in, or they were disbelieved, or the abuser told them that they had invited the abuse and would be punished if they told anyone, then they are likely to take on meanings such as 'It was my fault'; 'I am a bad little girl/boy'; 'I deserve to be punished' and 'People can't be trusted', which in turn give rise to feelings of shame, guilt and fear. No one should be exposed to abuse of any kind, and the responsibility for it remains firmly with the abuser. At the same time, we can see how the meaning that is attributed to these inexcusable actions has the potential to change their impact, for better or worse. However, as we'll also see, modifying meanings is not something we can necessarily do easily or quickly in the face of strong ideological pressures to view things in a particular way.

We have already shown in Chapter 5 that no two people's experience of threat is the same. The link between power and threat is not fixed or inevitable because of other aspects of the situation that may increase or reduce its impact. Adding in 'meaning' introduces another layer of complexity. This is another reason why we can't make simple cause–effect links between the events and circumstances of people's lives and the consequences in terms of distress or 'mental health problems'. Trauma and abuse can be crippling in their effects, but not everyone who is traumatised will later start to hear hostile voices or have extreme mood swings or self-harm, although some will. Poverty raises the risk of mental health difficulties, but not everyone who is poor will become what we might diagnose as 'depressed'. Equally, events that might seem, from the outside, less difficult can be extremely distressing to the person involved, depending on their significance and meaning for them. In addition, the PTMF shows how even the more fortunate among us, who may not have experienced obvious traumas, can end up struggling as a result of more subtle pressures and expectations and their meanings for us. 'Meaning' is the thread that holds all the other aspects of the PTMF together.

Table 6.1 below gives a list of common meanings that people give to distressing experiences.

Table 6.1: Meanings

Unsafe, afraid, attacked	Trapped
Abandoned, rejected	Defeated
Helpless, powerless	Failed, inferior
Hopeless	Guilty, blameworthy, responsible
Invaded	Betrayed
Controlled	Shamed, humiliated
Emotionally overwhelmed	Sense of injustice/unfairness
Emotionally 'empty'	Sense of meaninglessness
Bad, unworthy	Contaminated, evil.
Isolated, lonely	Alien, dangerous
Excluded, alienated	Different, abnormal

Most therapies are essentially about changing meanings (or, in psychological terms, 'cognitions' or 'schemas'). In other words, clients are helped to see, and eventually to believe, that the meanings they have understandably created about themselves, and about other people and the world, can gradually be transformed into different ones. This might involve a shift from 'symptom' to 'survival strategy' and perhaps also from an identity of 'mentally ill' to one of 'survivor of difficult circumstances'. Where some therapies may fall short is by focusing on meanings at a purely individual or family level. The risk is that people may then feel even worse about themselves because they are not able to change their 'negative cognitions' about being unemployed or badly housed or unable to buy things for their children. In some therapies, the message of self-blame and locating the problem within the person may be rather similar to the diagnostic one. In contrast, the PTMF aims to expand our understanding of meaning beyond traditional definitions and beyond the individual, as described below.

What do we mean by meaning?

People brought up in a Western or Westernised culture are likely to see meaning-making as a process that happens mainly inside your own head, based on words and language (we will discuss this further in Chapters 8 and 10). If this is your cultural background, you may also assume that 'thinking' is separate from 'feeling' – in fact, these two activities are often contrasted with each other – and that both are different from physical reactions. These taken-for-granted views are not necessarily accurate, and nor are they found in all cultures. The PTMF perspective challenges these and various other assumptions (see Chapter 3 of the main PTMF document).

Meanings arise from many sources, including our emotions and physical senses and the language we hear and learn. We can see this in relation to some of the meanings in Table 6.1. Shame is something we all experience at times, but it is often particularly damaging in people who have been psychiatrically diagnosed. At one level, shame is a belief that I am worthy of condemnation for who I am or what I have done. Equally, it is a strong emotion and, moreover, an emotion felt partly in the body, perhaps through a sense of tension or shrinking away from other people. The same applies to other meanings that are at the root of what we call mental health problems and are felt by all of us at times – anger, guilt, fear, despair, worthlessness and so on. Indeed, some cultures do not make a clear distinction between thought and feeling (Cromby, 2015). This is one of the many reasons why approaches such as CBT, which are based on the assumption that we can divide thoughts, feelings and beliefs into separate parcels and manipulate the relationships between them, may make little sense in non-Western cultures.

The PTMF emphasises that we need to look further than the inside of our heads if we want to understand how we create meanings about our lives. This brings us back to the discussion about ideological power in Chapter 4 of this book, where we argued that our meanings do not develop in a vacuum; they are influenced by the discourses of the society around us and the ideological interests that underpin those discourses. This means that personal meaning is never just a matter of individual choice; it is always something that we both 'make and find' (Shotter, 1993, cited in Johnstone & Boyle, 2018a, p.79).

When we learn language, we are at the same time taking on board all the values, norms, assumptions and expectations of the society and culture we inhabit. For example, we learn not only the terms for 'girl', 'boy', 'man' and 'woman' but about all the various ways that men and women are believed to differ, and all the ways they are expected, at a particular time and place in the world, to feel, behave and run their lives. As we saw in our earlier discussions, these messages are reinforced in numerous ways in our wider cultures, so that we also learn what are, or should be, the attributes of a 'good' parent, a 'normal' child, a 'happy family', and what counts as being successful, attractive and lovable or different, unacceptable and a failure, and so on. This often involves stereotypes about particular groups – people from African, Caribbean, Asian and other minority heritage in White-dominated societies; stereotypes about single parents, working mothers, people with a disability or an intellectual impairment, older adults, immigrants, refugees, the unemployed, people regarded as 'mentally ill', and many others.

We may assume that these beliefs are simply facts about the world. For example, until comparatively recently, it was accepted as fact that women were inferior to men and that White people were more intelligent than members of other ethnic groups.[1] Similarly, we may believe that we have come to these conclusions ourselves. This is not surprising because, as we've discussed, typically the messages are so widespread and subtle that it is hard to question them, and we may not even be aware that they are open to debate. However, if we can identify and trace back these meanings, we very often find that they are backed up by economic and other interests that are, in turn, reinforced through ideological power – in other words, the power to create, shape and impose meanings.

1. See the discussion on race and ethnicity in the main PTMF document, on pages 128–137.

Some real life examples of how meanings shape distress

Lucy Johnstone (one of the authors of this book) worked for many years with women survivors of rape and sexual abuse. The women's individual circumstances were different, but each was tormented by a similar sense of guilt, shame and self-blame. They were convinced that they ought to have fought back, or run away, or been in a different place, or worn different clothes, or anticipated what happened, or somehow made it stop, and so on. Each woman felt completely isolated in her shame and despair, and yet each woman was saying almost identical things.

It is not hard to work out why women end up with these beliefs and feelings. Psychologist Jessica Taylor has shown that blaming women for the sexual violence committed against them is deeply embedded in society at every level, from porn culture and gender stereotypes to beliefs about what counts as 'resisting' as opposed to 'inviting' the assault, and what counts as a 'real rape' (Eaton, 2019). The rape survivors she interviewed were all wrestling with these messages, even while knowing that they were unjust:

> When you have lived with something like that for so many years it's really difficult to change your way of thinking and you think you have but you haven't and it's still there because logically it doesn't make sense that you think that way, but you do. (Eaton, 2019)

While it is possible to work with these meanings in individual therapy and find some relief from the self-torment, the PTMF perspective suggests that we need to look more widely at the origins of these painful scripts. A more effective response, which originates from the women's movement, may be to invite women to meet in groups where they can track these meanings beyond the individual level, put responsibility back where it belongs and, in some cases, take action for social change. They may then be able to see how encouraging women to turn their distress and guilt inwards has allowed society as a whole to minimise and deny the horrific levels of violence and abuse in women's and girls' lives. In the sexual abuse survivor groups set up by Lucy Johnstone and her colleagues, some of the women attenders not only found significant relief from personal shame by sharing their previously hidden feelings but were later able to make use of their experiences by helping to train mental health staff about the impact of trauma (see the PTMF *Overview* document, Appendix 5).

As we've discussed in Chapter 4 of this book, one form of ideological power can be seen in the promotion of the dominant Western 'cultural narrative of distress' – in other words, the belief that distress is a kind of medical illness. Many women who have been harmed by experiences of abuse, like the ones described above, have been told that they have 'borderline personality disorder' (75% of people so labelled are women (APA, 2013, p.666)). This is one of the more stigmatising labels, because 'as a group we already feel sub-human, misunderstood and vulnerable, and now we are tarred with the brush of being bad as well as mad' (cited in Johnstone, 2014, p.68).

One study made the values and ideological messages underpinning this label very clear. A group of researchers examined the hidden values in the criteria on which the 'borderline personality disorder' diagnosis is based (Leising et al., 2009). They did this by taking the official 'symptoms' of 'personality disorder' and turning them into their opposites. For example, the symptom 'Is inhibited in new interpersonal situations because of feelings of inadequacy', by implication, suggests that a 'normal' person would be 'confident and relaxed in social situations.' By drawing out the implicit standards underpinning all these so-called symptoms, the researchers were able to show how someone with a 'normal', as opposed to a 'disordered', personality is meant to think, feel and behave. These included being 'self-reliant and independent', 'self-confident, but in a realistic manner' and 'sexually modest', along with 'getting along with others', 'looking for the good in people', 'enjoying social relationships and activities' and so on.

We might agree with some of this but, as the researchers note, in doing so we need to be clear that we are not making a medical judgement but imposing a certain set of cultural values, to the detriment of those who feel and behave differently – as suggested by the fact that one of the implicit criteria is the requirement to be 'conventional'. The hidden criteria associated with the specific diagnosis of 'borderline personality disorder' are even more worrying. In the research, these turned out to include 'Be able to control your impulses and emotions; display anger only when appropriate, and with moderate intensity; have trust in other people' (in other words, the opposite of the official criteria of 'Impulsive behavior; inappropriate, intense anger' and so on).

The clear implication is that a woman labelled with 'borderline personality disorder' has officially been judged as lacking in self-control, too distrustful, too angry and so on, by the standards of society. The message of the diagnosis is that there is no justification for feeling so upset and angry about what has happened to her. We can see very clearly how this diagnosis draws on gender stereotypes that have the effect of inducing shame, invalidating the woman's experience, placing the burden on her to feel and behave differently, and locating her as the source of the problem (see the discussion on invalidation in Chapter 4 of this book). A new set of meanings has been imposed on her, wrapped up in medical language.

It goes without saying that men too can be victims of abuse, and that this typically results in slightly different although equally damaging meanings to do with feeling weak and powerless and thus 'less of a man' (Jones, 2020).[2] Men are over-represented in the criminal justice system, in drug and alcohol services, and among the single homeless. The section on sex and gender in the main PTMF report (pp.124–128) notes that all men do not have equal access to power, since they may face inequalities in terms of class, ethnicity, sexuality and (dis)ability and so on. It is also true that even men who have advantages and privileges can be psychologically harmed by conventional gender stereotypes.

One of the adversities that may have a particularly powerful impact on men, given their traditional role as main wage-earner and provider, is loss of employment. Danny Whittaker's experience, which he has described in a powerful podcast,[3] illustrates this point. His breakdown was triggered by the collapse of his nightclub. He had shown extraordinary levels of determination in setting it up at the age of 23, renovating the building almost singlehandedly and

2. See Owen Jones's article in *The Guardian* about the experiences of men who have been raped: www.theguardian.com/commentisfree/2020/jan/16/male-rape-victims-sexual-abuse-support

3. Danny Whittaker's podcast, in which he interviews leading psychologists, philosophers, academics and authors in the mental health field, can be found at www.podcasts.com/my-own-worst-enemy-psychology-philosophy-mental-health

working round the clock for months. But it was around the time of the economic crash in 2008, and everything conspired against him. When his credit was withdrawn, he was unable to save the club. This was the start of a descent into incapacitating anxiety that led to being virtually housebound and nearly destroyed his relationship with his partner. These circumstances would have been hard for anyone, but for Danny, who saw himself as a fairly traditional man, there was an extra layer of torment. He had taken on the belief that 'If you try hard enough you will be rewarded', and in his own words 'I could not forgive myself' for what he perceived as a humiliating personal failure.

There is nothing wrong with working hard to achieve, but when this message chimes so closely with wider neoliberal messages about resilience, aspiration and pulling yourself up by your own bootstraps (as we discussed in Chapter 4), and when the economic odds are stacked against you, you are set up to fall into self-punishment and self-blame. When Danny read the PTMF some years later, he was finally able to take on a different perspective. As he put it:

> The PTMF forced me to take seriously the possibility that what I considered wholesale personal failures that I'd brought upon myself due to incompetence were probably better understood as circumstances forced upon me over which I had zero control. I discovered that my guilt struggled to persist under proper scrutiny.

If we accept these arguments, it will not be surprising to learn that Black, Asian and other minority ethnic groups living in White-dominated societies have been found to be particularly likely to construct meanings about being unsafe and the world being dangerous and to react with extreme suspicion and hypervigilance – or 'paranoia', to use the clinical term. More generally, 'paranoia' has well established links to neglect, physical and sexual abuse, bullying, institutional care and unsafe environments, making it, as researchers have commented, 'understandable, and, indeed, adaptive' (Shevlin et al., 2015). Young Black men living in urban environments have especially high rates of this form of 'psychosis' (see, for example, Rosen et al., 2017). More than 20 years ago, psychiatrists Roland

Littlewood and Maurice Lipsedge concluded that so-called delusional beliefs among members of these groups about being persecuted, spied on and so on may be 'merely a strong reiteration of the experience of discrimination' (Littlewood & Lipsedge, 1997). In other words, meanings about lack of safety are fundamentally accurate for people living in deprived areas and facing numerous forms of racism.

A 2019 BBC documentary shows that nothing much has changed (Harewood, 2019). Actor David Harewood discussed racism as a factor in his 'psychotic' breakdown, which included extreme fear and suspicion:

> Although I was conscious of myself as a Black man, it really wasn't until I got out of drama school that the world said to me: 'You are Black. Your aspirations, your dreams, your hopes, are now restricted.'

In a state of agitation and distress, he was held down by six policemen and sedated. One of the professionals he interviewed in the documentary pointed to 'images of Black men as violent, hypermasculinity, so... when a Black man presents in crisis sometimes people's ideas about what Black men are like overshadow the person that's in front of them'. These attitudes have ideologically driven roots. In his book *The Protest Psychosis: How schizophrenia became a black disease*, psychiatrist Jonathan Metzl (2010) shows how the civil rights movement in the US was paralleled by a rise in the numbers of African-American men diagnosed with 'schizophrenia'. This increase was facilitated by adding 'hostility' and 'aggression' to the description of 'schizophrenia' in *DSM-II* in 1968. These men's assertive demands for equality could thus be redefined as 'mental illness'.

David Harewood, like many who break down, did not have a history of specific trauma – rather, he experienced what one of the documentary's commentators described as 'the everyday struggle' of being Black in a predominantly White society. The PTMF shows how distress can be experienced by people without an apparent trauma history, due to the impact of ideological power filtered through unquestioned and unrealistic social norms and expectations. These stories are often less obvious to the person themselves, to those around them and to the professionals they may encounter ('Nothing bad has happened to me – I should be happy' and so on), making it seem more reasonable to assume they have been hit by a randomly occurring 'mental illness'.

We can illustrate this by thinking about the rising tide of distress among our children and young people. While some of this is linked to poverty, bullying and other difficult circumstances (NHS Digital, 2018), many of these children come from loving and materially comfortable homes. It is all too tempting to 'explain' their distress in terms of the ever-expanding categories listed in the *DSM*, such as ADHD. But in doing so, we risk obscuring the many factors that make life exceptionally difficult for our young people. Child psychiatrist Sami Timimi has written extensively about the 'McDonaldisation of childhood' (Timimi, 2009). He shows how neoliberal ideals encourage commercialism and exam-based, target-driven schooling, and how families under stress are much less able to offer secure backgrounds and enough parental attention and supportive links to the local community. Meanwhile, social media is a powerful and destructive medium for reinforcing idealised messages about how young people ought to look, feel and conduct their lives. The end results are not surprising. Buffeted one way and another by these pressures, with insecure job futures and no certainty about being able to afford their own homes or provide a stable background for their own families in the future, the meanings that young people in the UK often develop about themselves are of worthlessness, sadness, hopelessness, anxiety and failure (Johnson, 2018; McInerney, 2019).

Cross-cultural meanings

So far this chapter has focused mainly on the discourses and ideological meanings that arise within Western and Westernised industrialised societies, particularly those like the US and the UK that have been most influenced by neoliberalism. Globalisation means that these assumptions are increasingly found across the world. The PTMF also challenges us to question some of the most deeply held meanings that have shaped Western thought – those to do with identity and the very nature of who we are, as we will discuss in Chapter 10. It brings us face to face with profound questions such as:

- What is the relationship between thinking and feeling, mind and body?

- What is the relationship between the individual and the social group?

- What do we mean by the idea of a unique 'self' with its own identity?

- What is the role of spirituality?

- What is the relationship between human beings and the natural world?

We invite readers to reflect on the following examples.

The Iban people of Malaysia have no equivalent of the psychiatric concept of 'thought disorder' because they do not clearly distinguish between thinking (in the internal Western sense) and talking. An anthropologist described his struggle to explain to the Iban what he meant by thoughts, given that they 'have a more embodied and interactional notion of thinking... the closest equivalent to the Western notion of thinking is experienced as arising from the heart-liver region, and it is intimately tied up with emotion, desire and will'. He concluded that his questions were based on 'a Western cultural concept of personhood, which gives a privileged place to internal mental life as a defining feature of the person... recognised as located in the brain, and... experienced as disembodied' (Barrett, 2004, cited in Johnstone & Boyle, 2018a, pp. 96 & 99).

And this is an example from Zanzibar, where experiences that we might label as 'schizophrenia' present themselves very differently. The indigenous people's sense of the self has much looser boundaries than in the West and they do not see body, mind and spirit as separate. They frequently experience themselves as being inhabited by visiting spirits, which is not seen as abnormal in itself. However, the local social norms promote calm, reserved and non-confrontational behaviour, whereas sometimes these spirits are noisy, rude, emotional and selfish. The resulting outbursts are usually explained as a form of madness caused by spirit possession (McGruder, 2004). The very different notions of selfhood in Zanzibar have resulted in a dilemma for researchers trying to assimilate these experiences into the Western concept of 'schizophrenia'.

The PTMF is intended to accommodate and respect such experiences, unusual as they may be to those brought up in Western traditions, without seeking to translate them into diagnostic language such as 'thought disorder' and 'schizophrenia'. Instead, the PTMF argues that we need to expand our understandings of how distress may arise and how it may be healed.

The epistemic injustice of denying people's meanings by imposing diagnostic categories is multiplied many times when they are applied to indigenous groups with a history of colonisation. An Australian professor of psychology, Bernard Guerin, has shown how the criteria for 'borderline personality disorder', as applied to Aboriginal people, are a shocking denial of their legitimate anger and despair at generations of socially-sanctioned brutality (Fromene et al, 2014), as follows:

> DSM criterion: '*Frantic attempts to avoid real or imagined abandonment.*'
> Reality: Decades of forced separation from caregivers and family.
>
> DSM criterion: '*Identity disturbance: marked and unstable self-image or sense of self.*'
> Reality: Loss of family, kinship system, land and country.
>
> DSM criterion: '*Chronic feelings of emptiness.*'
> Reality: Grief and hopelessness from cumulative loss, trauma and disempowerment.
>
> DSM criterion: '*Inappropriate, intense anger or difficulty controlling anger.*'
> Reality: Legacy of collective trauma through victimisation, forced assimilation, discrimination from judicial, health and education systems.

We will return to these issues in Chapters 8 and 10.

A note on shame

The analysis in Chapter 4 and here may help us to understand why shame as an emotional meaning, along with related meanings to do with failure, difference and exclusion, is so strongly associated with a diagnosis of all kinds of 'mental illness', in contrast to the reaction to most physical health problems. As one person put it, 'Let's just say I have a case of shame – I really do' (cited in Warner, 2004). Shame has been described as both the most social of emotions and the most hidden and 'un-speakable' (Frost, 2016). We feel shame when we judge ourselves through the imagined disapproving eyes of others. This makes it a powerful social mechanism for promoting or discouraging certain beliefs, experiences and ways of behaving and, as we've seen in Chapter 4, we are all increasingly encouraged to monitor ourselves for signs of failure to conform. Since, as we have also seen, psychiatric diagnoses are ultimately based on a judgement that you have deviated from expected social norms and standards, some degree of shame is almost inevitable as a response. You have, in effect, been told, 'Your feelings and reactions are viewed by your social group as beyond what is reasonable, understandable or acceptable.'

Human beings have a basic psychological need to belong to a social group, and it is devastating to feel excluded. In one person's words, a psychiatric diagnosis makes you 'an outcast in society' (quoted in Johnstone, 2014, p.67). From this point of view, anti-stigma campaigns, with their message that mental health problems are 'an illness like any other', are doomed to failure, as a great deal of research shows.[4] We know when we are being subjected to social shaming, and no amount of dressing it up will take that away. The real answer to stigma is to drop the diagnostic system itself. Even if we are yet to do this as a society, we should be offering alternatives to taking on these diagnostic identities. The PTMF supports people to make that choice, if they wish, by tracing back the toxic meanings of shame, deficit, difference and failure to their ideological roots.

---

4. See the discussion on anti-stigma campaigns in the main PTMF document, on pages 274–276. A useful blog on the topic, 'When the ads don't work', by David Harper and Anne Cooke, can be found at https://blogs.canterbury.ac.uk/discursive/when-the-ads-dont-work

We have seen that at the root of nearly every experience of distress is a clash between (often hidden) assumptions about how we should think, feel, behave and live our lives, and our failure (whether actual or perceived) to live up to these standards and ideals. Despite the actual obstacles we may be facing, and the unrealistic nature of what we are aspiring to, this tends to result in a range of painful emotional meanings in which we turn the blame on ourselves. Diagnosis – and increasingly, self-diagnosis via the media and the internet – reinforces the message that the problems lie within us by imposing an ideologically-driven medical narrative, with its own associated meanings. The labels offer what has been described as 'cruel optimism' – in other words, an idea that promises understanding and healing but actually becomes an obstacle to achieving what you need and hope for (Berlant, 2011). In fact it prevents us – at an individual and a societal level – from questioning the assumptions that have led us into difficulty in the first place. In the words of psychologist Dorothy Rowe: 'In the final analysis, power is the right to have your definition of reality prevail over all other people's definition of reality' (Rowe, 1990, cited in Johnstone, 2014, p.88). Challenging and changing these meanings and this version of reality is an important starting point that helps to open up new choices and new ways of moving forward.

In contrast to the diagnostic model, the PTMF encourages us to trace our personal meanings back to the social expectations and ideological pressures from which they arise. This is not an easy process, since by definition these norms and standards can:

> … be regarded as forming the very fabric of our existence…
> [T]o step outside such expectations and 'rules' is extremely difficult. They form the backdrop to the social world in which we live… and so can be seen to operate at a level of *unawareness*. (Hagan & Donnison, 1999, original italics)

Exercise 5, in combination with consideration of the role of ideological power in Exercise 3, may help to us to become more aware of these hidden standards and pressures.

Exercise 5

'How did you make sense of it?' (What is the meaning of these experiences to you?)

Look at the table of meanings we have reproduced on page 72. Think about whether they seem to fit from your point of view, or that of the person you are working with or supporting. As before, you are likely to find that some of the meanings are already implied by your responses to the questions about power and threat. However, there may be others that you wish to add or to jot down in the relevant section of the template on page 91 of the online guided discussion (at **www.bps.org.uk/sites/www.bps.org.uk/files/Policy/Policy%20-%20Files/PTM%20Guided%20Discussion.pdf**).

If this exercise is in any way difficult or upsetting, take a break and use the ideas and resources from Exercise 2 in Chapter 3.

Chapter 7
'What did you have to do to survive?' (What kinds of threat response are you using?)

In Chapter 5, we discussed the various forms of threat we can face as human beings and the factors that can make them easier or harder to survive. In this chapter, we show how people try to survive the negative operation of power and the meaning-based threats that result from it by drawing on a range of threat responses. In other words, we do whatever we can, with whatever resources we have, to meet our needs and manage our lives. This part of the PTMF draws from trauma-informed ideas and practices, among other sources, which we summarise briefly below.

The trauma-informed approach[1]

The large body of work known as the trauma-informed approach (TIA) integrates research about the importance of early relationships (attachment theory), the effects of traumatic events on the mind and body and the impact of the wider social environment. As such, it presents a major and convincing challenge to the biomedical model and is increasingly influencing policy and services. Trauma-informed practice is recognised in policy documents, especially in Scotland and Wales, and some services are adopting its ideas (Sweeney et al., 2016).[2]

1. For a more detailed discussion, see the main PTMF document (pp.175–181 and 187–189). An excellent overview of the approach can be found in Bessel van der Kolk's book (2014) *The Body Keeps the Score*.

2. For developments in Wales, see www.wales.nhs.uk/sitesplus/888/page/88504, and in Scotland, www.gov.scot/publications/adverse-childhood-experiences/

The TIA demonstrates that, as many of us have always known, people who experience extreme forms of distress often have histories of trauma, such as emotional and physical abuse and neglect, sexual abuse, domestic violence, bullying, and many other adversities. It has been shown that, on average, the more trauma someone has suffered, especially in early life (where the term Adverse Childhood Experiences (ACEs) is used), the more likely they are to do poorly on a whole range of physical health, mental health, employment, educational and social outcomes.[3]

Research has shown, again not surprisingly, that we need to take into account stressors such as unsafe urban environments, racial discrimination or seeing someone being beaten, stabbed or shot, which may be more common in areas of high deprivation. These factors are traumatic in their own right, as well as increasing the likelihood of abuse, violence and neglect in personal and family relationships (see, for example, The Philadelphia ACE Survey, n.d.). One of the most useful aspects of the TIA is the way it reframes psychiatric 'symptoms' as threat responses and survival strategies used by our minds and bodies to protect us from the impact of adversities. However unusual or disabling they may be, these strategies originally served a useful purpose in the face of threats to our physical, emotional or social wellbeing.

There is some evidence that the impact of unresolved trauma can be passed down the generations, so that the children and grandchildren of people who have survived adversities are also affected. This is known as transgenerational trauma or, in situations such as war, slavery, natural disaster, colonialism and genocide, where a whole population is affected, historical trauma (van der Zee, 2019). More recently, global warming and its related effects have been acknowledged as a new and profound threat to the very existence of the planet. The term 'climate trauma' (sometimes called climate distress, eco fear or eco trauma) is used to describe how this is experienced and responded to at all levels, from individual to global (Woodbury, 2019).

The PTMF draws on the TIA, among other sources, while also seeing it as having some potential limitations, depending on how it is understood and implemented (for critiques, see

---

3. For an overview of current research, see www.acestoohigh.com

Sweeney & Taggart (2018) and Turner (2019)). For example, the TIA sometimes uses diagnostic language such as 'PTSD' or 'dissociative disorder'. There is a risk that 'trauma' is seen as referring to specific abusive events, at the expense of acknowledging equally damaging background contexts, such as poverty and racial discrimination. For this reason, the PTMF generally uses the term 'adversity' instead. Trauma-informed work does not always make clear the links to the wider power contexts of economic inequality and social injustice, although some of it does. Finally, the PTMF acknowledges that not everyone in distress has experienced a traumatic event or events, in the usual meaning of the word. However, this may not be enough to protect us from the more subtle pressures and expectations of modern industrialised societies, which are explored within the PTMF.

Threat responses and the role of the body

The PTMF includes the physical aspects of our experiences. As we pointed out in Chapter 3, everything we feel or do, whether seen as 'normal' or 'abnormal', has biological aspects. We could not watch television, enjoy a meal or chat to our friends without having physical bodies to enable us to do so. However, as we've also seen, the involvement of our bodies does not necessarily mean that any particular experience is best understood as a medical illness.

The TIA shows how adversity affects our bodies, brains and minds but does not make simplistic statements about biological causes, such as chemical imbalances and genetic flaws. Instead, it takes findings from neuroscientific research to demonstrate how human beings draw on various physical reactions that have evolved to keep us safe and help us meet our needs in the face of trauma and adversities. These ways of reacting to threat are sometimes called 'symptoms' but, from both trauma-informed and the PTMF perspectives, they are seen as threat responses and survival strategies. For example, faced with dangerous or emotionally overwhelming events and situations, we may go into an automatic fight/flight/freeze response to protect ourselves. Our bodies may become hyperalert, releasing high levels of chemicals like adrenalin and cortisol to prepare us to fight or run away. Alternatively, we may 'freeze' like a rabbit in the headlights (see the Cwm Taf Morgannwg self-help leaflets for more information about the impact of trauma on the mind and body[4]).

The TIA also shows how a process called 'dissociation' can enable us to cut off from feelings and memories of events that are too much to bear at the time. We have the capacity to store these memories in a different way in the brain, where they may be lost to our conscious minds. The more limited the power resources available to us, the more likely it is that we will have to resort to these kinds of strategies. Dissociation is sometimes called 'the escape when there is no escape'. For example, a small child may have no way of avoiding abuse by an adult except by going somewhere else in their minds. Similarly, adults in relatively powerless situations, perhaps trapped in a violent relationship or an unsafe living situation because of poverty, may resort to hypervigilance, withdrawal or low mood and numbing their feelings as their only options.

However, these aspects of our experiences are not lost forever, and they may 'leak out' in various ways that may be labelled as 'symptoms'. For example, hearing hostile and disturbing voices is often related to unresolved emotional trauma, and the voices may sound like or use the same phrases as the person's abusers (Longden et al., 2012). A diagnosis of depression can sometimes indicate that we have not been able to grieve for a loss. Compulsion to repeat certain rituals may help us to avoid earlier feelings of being out of control. We can also employ more deliberate strategies to cope with overwhelming emotions, conflicts and memories, such as restricting our eating, or avoiding relationships, or using alcohol, or self-injuring.

Table 7.1 gives examples of the many reactions that might, for some people in some circumstances, be best understood as threat responses (Johnstone & Boyle, 2018b, p.40). It is not an exhaustive list, and you may be able to think of other examples. Many of these threat responses, such as feeling suicidal or hearing hostile voices, are typically labelled as symptoms of a 'mental illness'. Others are more likely to be seen as socially acceptable or 'normal'.

---

4. See https://cwmtafmorgannwg.wales/services/mental-health/stabilisation-pack/

Table 7.1: Threat responses

Preparing to 'fight' or attack	Attention/concentration problems
Preparing to 'flee', escape, seek safety	Confused/unstable self-image/sense of self
Freeze response	Confused/confusing speech and communication
Hypervigilance, startle responses, insomnia	Self-injury of various types
Panic, phobias	Self-neglect
Fragmented memory encoding	Dieting, self-starvation
Memory suppression (amnesia)	Bingeing, over-eating
Hearing voices	Self-silencing
Dissociating (losing track of time/place; various degrees of splitting of awareness)	Mourning, grieving
Depersonalisation, derealisation	Self-blame and self-punishment
Flashbacks	Body hatred
Nightmares	Compulsive thoughts
NEAD ('non-epileptic attack disorder')	Carrying out rituals & other 'safety behaviours'
Emotional numbing, flattening, indifference	Collecting, hoarding
Bodily numbing	Avoidance of/compulsive use of sexuality
Submitting, appeasing	Impulsivity
Giving up, 'learned helplessness', low mood	Anger, rage
Protesting, weeping, clinging	Aggression and violence
Suspicious thoughts	Suicidal thinking and actions
Emotional regression, withdrawal	Distrust of others
'High' or extreme moods; rapid mood changes ('emotional dysregulation')	Feeling entitled
Holding unusual beliefs	Reduced empathy
Having unusual visual, olfactory, tactile sensations	Distrust
	Avoiding threat triggers.
	Striving, perfectionism, 'drive' response
	Using drugs, alcohol, smoking
	Overworking, over-exercising, etc.

Somatic sensations – tension, dizziness, physical pain, tinnitus, sensations of heat or cold, exhaustion, skin irritation, gastrointestinal problems and many other bodily reactions	Giving up hope/loss of faith in the world
	Relational strategies; rejection and maintaining emotional distance; seeking care and attachments; taking on caring roles; isolation/avoidance of others; dominance, seeking control over others; and so on.
Emotional defences: grandiosity, denial, externalising, projection, idealisation	
Intellectualisation (avoiding feelings and bodily sensations)	Ruminating, reflecting, anticipating, imagining, interpreting, meaning-making

The PTMF perspective on threat responses

From both a PTMF and a trauma-informed perspective, threat responses are there for a good reason and may still be protective if the situation has not changed. They are necessary and creative strategies that we all use at times for protection and survival, not simply psychiatric 'symptoms' to be suppressed with drugs. However, people may need help to move on from responses that served them well when they were in greatest danger but may end up causing problems in their own right.

In summary, the message of the both the TIA and the PTMF is: 'You can be proud of surviving very difficult circumstances in the best way you could at the time, using the resources that were available to you. These strategies may no longer be needed or useful, and with the right kind of support you can learn to leave them behind.'

The PTMF perspective on threat responses is expanded below.

Threat responses are on a spectrum

Because we are all members of the same species with the same core needs, we have evolved to respond to threats in similar ways, and we all share some of the more instinctive bodily based reactions, such as the fight/flight/freeze response. However, threat responses range across a continuum; some are under a greater degree of control, even if they are not always easy to stop. Thus, responses like drinking alcohol, using street drugs, self-harming, avoiding going out, carrying out rituals and so on are more consciously adopted and depend partly on our social contexts, what we have learned from others, and what people around us are doing.

Threat responses are shaped by our power resources

As we saw in Chapter 5 on threat, our threat responses depend partly on what options we have. We can see the results of this in the criminal justice system. The less access you have to conventional or approved forms of power, the more likely you are to adopt socially disruptive strategies. Those of us who are more fortunate may express our frustration at injustice by petitions and campaigning; others whose lives are more directly affected may resort to stealing or violence. This does not mean we should excuse such behaviour, but it shows that people will use whatever limited forms of power are available to them.

Threat responses may be socially valued

Table 7.1 includes some responses that are unlikely to be diagnosed as 'symptoms' by mental health professionals because they are approved by society. We have seen that decisions about what counts as a 'mental illness' are essentially based on social judgements about acceptable ways of thinking, feeling and behaving. For example, most Westerners live in a culture that praises and promotes working long hours and certain standards of appearance. This means that we are likely to admire the executive who spends 70 hours a week at his desk, or the female celebrity whose life is devoted to maintaining perfect weight and fashion choices. But it is possible that, in both cases, these individuals are actually driven by lack of confidence or difficulties in personal relationships – in other words, that these ways of behaving are actually threat responses. Of course, there is nothing wrong with working hard or wanting to look your best, and whether a particular way of living your life is understood partly or entirely as a threat response is something only the person themselves can decide. But problems may arise when the main function of these ways of behaving is to avoid emotional conflict and pain, which is why people may find it hard to act differently, even when the negatives outweigh the positives.

Conversely, many of the experiences that might earn you a psychiatric label in Westernised settings may be important aspects of your life and identity – neither a 'symptom' nor a threat response. We know, for example, that the voices people hear can be supportive and helpful to them, and there are cultures in which this ability is socially accepted and valued (Read, 2016). Rather than impairing a person's life, it may enhance it.

Threat responses vary across historical time

Threat responses are shaped by culture, especially as we move further up the spectrum from the more biologically-based ones. This explains why they may change so much historically, because cultures and cultural meanings (including gender roles and expectations) also change. Nowadays we do not see the 'hysteria' that afflicted so many Victorian women, and even the reactions we know as 'PTSD' look very different from the 'shellshock' of the First World War. The PTMF suggests that, at any given moment, people 'unconsciously seize on a form of expression that is a culturally-recognised signal of suffering. Newspapers and journals write about it, people start to seek help for it, and… perceptions of the new problem are shaped' (Watters, 2011, p.35). These changes are very hard to explain from a medical perspective (pneumonia, tuberculosis and heart disease present in much the same way as they did 100 years ago), but they make sense within a meaning-based approach like the PTMF. The suffering is real, but the forms in which it is expressed evolve surprisingly quickly. We (the authors) of this book hardly ever came across self-harm, anorexia, bulimia or what would now be called 'borderline personality disorder' at the start of our careers. Similarly, only 50 years ago, 'depressive disorder', now said to be the world's leading cause of disability, was thought to be rare (Horwitz, 2010).

Threat responses vary across cultures

As we discussed in Chapter 2, diagnostic systems have a great deal of difficulty explaining cultural differences in the way distress is expressed. The solution adopted by the compilers of the fourth edition of the *DSM* (*DSM-IV*) was to place many of these strange – from a Western perspective – manifestations of distress in an Appendix titled 'Culture-bound syndromes', to await the research that would decide which group of 'mental illnesses' they belonged to. From a PTMF viewpoint, this simply shows the extent to which the Western psychiatric viewpoint is assumed to be the objective, universal and 'true' one. Anything else is seen as a primitive or exotic variation of the 'real' disorder.

In contrast, the PTMF shows that all expressions of distress are 'culture-bound'. In fact, some of the more familiar Western presentations – such as self-starvation/anorexia – would look equally strange to members of a society that struggles to feed its population. From a PTMF perspective, the threat responses that are more biologically based and automatic can be expected to be similar across all cultural groups, but they will vary as we move up the spectrum and there is more potential for shaping by local customs and meanings. The resulting expressions of distress may seem very unusual to Western eyes. For example, in Japan, a society that places very strong emphasis on conformity and deference to others, people may suffer from *taijin kyofusho*, defined in *DSM-5* as an intense fear of offending or harming others leading to withdrawal from social situations. These kinds of phenomena do not present a problem from a PTMF viewpoint – in fact they are predicted and expected.

Threat responses have functions and purposes

There is a great deal of research, both psychiatric and psychological, into the origins of what the PTMF calls threat responses, usually phrased in terms such as 'What causes voice-hearing/low mood/ compulsive rituals/mood swings?' and so on. The PTMF argues that there cannot be universal explanations for why people feel anxious or suicidal or hear critical voices, why they hoard possessions or injure themselves, or why they fear that they are being persecuted and spied on, and so on. It is true that there are likely to be common themes in a particular culture, because those people will be influenced by the same shared meanings. For example, restricting your eating is often associated in Western societies with a need to feel in control, although this does not apply everywhere (see Watters, 2011, Chapter 1). Self-harm may be a common way for women to express anger if gender role expectations in a particular society discourage them from showing it more directly. However, it may also have many other meanings and functions.

From a PTMF viewpoint, then, it makes far more sense to ask what *functions and purposes* these reactions are serving for a person in a particular situation, rather than looking for specific medical or psychological *causes*. Sometimes the same response has several functions (for example, self-harm may help to relieve feelings, distract from emotional pain and fulfil a need to punish oneself). Sometimes several responses are serving the same purpose (for example, there may be many ways of punishing yourself). Sometimes the functions change over time. This links back to the core needs discussed in Chapter 5. Threat responses arise when we feel there is a serious risk that our core needs will not be met, and so they may be used for a huge array of purposes: to manage overwhelming feelings, protect us from physical danger, keep a sense of control, protect us from loss, hurt, rejection or abandonment, seek or hold onto safe relationships, hold onto a sense of self and identity, find a place for ourselves in social groups, meet our emotional needs, communicate a need for care and help, and find meaning and purpose in our life.

Threat responses can operate at the level of whole societies

The opening section on trauma-informed approaches notes the increasing amount of interest in the impact of trauma across whole generations or social groups. Judith Herman, in her classic book *Trauma and Recovery* (2001) argues that 'Denial, repression and dissociation operate on a social, as well as an individual level' (p.2), enabling the true extent of trauma to be denied and its victims to be silenced. Large-scale calamities such as war, slavery, colonialism, genocide and natural disasters leave emotional scars on whole groups of people. More recently, it has been argued that climate trauma, the ever-present threat to our whole way of life in which we are all 'both perpetrators and victims', has created a constant background state of fight, flight, fright, dissociation and denial in all of us, for which the only solution is collective awareness and action (Woodbury, 2019).

Here are some reflections on the PTMF's perspective on threat responses. The first is from one of the service-user consultants to the PTMF, whose feedback is reported in the main PTMF document:

> Intuitively, I always understood my experiences this way. How scared, suspicious and fearful I was made sense to me. I'd experienced various threats, including my first memory,

pretty much constantly throughout my life in all the different spheres I existed, and another dramatic threat on the day I started to hear voices… My voices, constantly threatening to harm me, and berating me as justification for why they would harm me, felt like an expression of the fear I'd spent my life denying I felt, and mirrored the general pattern of threats I'd experienced.

The second is from a social worker who encountered the PTMF during her training:

Claire describes herself as having been 'to the brink of insanity' after the birth of her daughter but says that 'The Power Threat Meaning Framework has been instrumental in my recovery.' She was given various diagnoses on the basis of threat responses including 'dissociating, nightmares, flashbacks, suspicious thoughts, suicidal thoughts, using alcohol, poor concentration, muscle spasms etc. The PTMF showed me that "abnormal behaviour and experiences can be seen as intelligible responses to our current circumstances", and she now feels that the Framework has helped her to 'find meaning to my experiences' in contrast to a system that simply wanted to diagnose her. 'Not one health professional asked WHY I was feeling like this. I vowed to myself that, if I survived this, I would go back to school and try help women that so desperately needed help.' (Claire McClorey, personal communication)

Linking threats and threat responses

One of the main aims of the PTMF is to put back the links between threats and threat responses. This is because, if the process is pursued far enough, it inevitably results in restoring the meaningful connections between personal/family/community distress and social inequality and injustice.

In some ways, linking threats and threat responses should be an obvious way to look at distress. We are not surprised that when a loved one dies, their relatives are grief-stricken; that when a child loses her parent in a crowd, she becomes anxious; that when someone is bullied, they are tearful and afraid or that, in the face of domestic violence or combat, people are anxious and hypervigilant. The connections are obvious. Similarly, in a wider context, few would be surprised to hear that rates of 'depression' are higher in deprived areas where people have more reasons to be miserable, or that racial discrimination is bad for our wellbeing. Add several of these factors together, because very few people in mental health services have experienced single adversities, and again, it is not surprising that, if you have faced a number of these problems, you are more likely to end up with a psychiatric diagnosis.

But at that point, the links seem to be lost. As we saw in Chapter 4, a mental health professional will certainly take a history if you are referred to a service, and you may be told that your life events were a 'trigger' for your 'mental illness', in line with what is called a biopsychosocial or vulnerability-stress model. However, from then on, interventions are likely to focus on 'treating' the 'symptoms', mainly with psychiatric drugs, while the full impact and meaning of your story is hidden behind a psychiatric label. You may be lucky enough to be offered talking therapy, but even then, the dominant approach (CBT) is typically focused on the individual and their current 'symptoms' and delivered alongside psychiatric drugs. The PTMF recognises that psychiatric drugs can be helpful, as can CBT strategies for managing anxiety, challenging negative thoughts and so on. However, it argues that psychotherapeutic approaches based on individualising, deficit-based assumptions have as many limitations as psychiatric ones.

The PTMF discusses a number of reasons why it may sometimes be very difficult to make links between threats and threat responses. For example, the threats may have occurred a long time ago, or are not accessible to the person's conscious memory, or the person may be too distrustful or ashamed to disclose them. The threats may be so numerous and the threat responses so varied that it is hard to see how they are connected. The threats may be socially acceptable – such as pressure to achieve good exam results or send young children to boarding school – and thus harder to recognise. The threat responses may take a form that is at first sight hard to make sense of, such as very unusual beliefs or experiences. Supporting people to make these links through therapy requires a great deal of empathy, persistence and skill, and we hope that the exercises in this book will be another way of helping you to do this.

Having said all this, the PTMF argues that the biggest barrier to restoring these links is the diagnostic model itself, which imposes a powerful expert narrative of individual deficit and 'illness.' This blinds both the person and those who are trying to help them. Nowadays it is increasingly likely that people will, in effect, diagnose themselves through the internet or a 'mental health awareness' course at work or school, or a self-help group. The diagnostic narrative is everywhere, as the official figure of 'one in four' people experiencing 'mental illness' creeps towards two in three and, inevitably, reaches four in four. Meanwhile, as prescriptions and waiting lists rise, our increasingly individualistic, materialistic, competitive and unequal society continues along the same path, disconnected from the consequences. As we phrase it in the PTMF *Overview* (p.31):

- There is resistance at all levels of society to recognising the prevalence of threats and the negative impacts of power.

- There are many vested personal, family, professional, organisational, community, business, economic and political interests in disconnecting threat from threat response and thus preserving the 'medical illness' model.

- These influences combine to deprive people of a socially shared framework of thought within which they can make sense of their own experiences in their own terms.

The end result is that experiences of trauma and adversity may be literally 'unspeakable' because they 'take place outside the realm of socially validated reality' (Herman, 2001, p.8). People may lack, or be actively denied, the knowledge, ideas and vocabulary to come to their own understanding of their life struggles. In other words, they may experience epistemic injustice (as described in Chapter 4.) A brief glance at social media discussions about 'mental health' will confirm that there is a strong backlash against the growing number of professionals and service users who are starting to demand the right to question the diagnostic model. One of the aims of the PTMF is to give people the information and resources to do this, if they so wish, and to make their experiences speakable.

We have now covered the core PTMF questions. The next chapter will show how the emerging stories prompted by these questions can be seen as part of a wider set of patterns in distress. In the meantime, you may wish to reflect on your own use of threat responses by doing the exercise below.

Exercise 6

'What did you have to do to survive?' (What kinds of threat response are you using?)

Look at the table of threat responses on page 90–91. We all behave or react in these ways at times, and often this is not a problem, or it might even be helpful. You can use the table to identify some of the most common or troublesome reactions to power and threat that apply to you or the person you are working with or supporting and what purpose they are serving. There may be other responses that you wish to add or jot down in the relevant section of the template on page 91 of the guided discussion (at **www.bps.org.uk/sites/www. bps.org.uk/files/Policy/Policy%20-%20Files/PTM%20Guided%20 Discussion.pdf**).

If this exercise is in any way difficult or upsetting, take a break and use the ideas and resources from Exercise 2 in Chapter 3.

Chapter 8
General patterns in distress

By this point in the book, we hope you will have:

- an appreciation of the problems with the diagnostic approach to distress

- a grasp of the basic principles of the PTMF and how they differ from medical ones

- an understanding of what the PTMF means by power, threat, meaning and threat responses

- some thoughts about what your own struggles, or the struggles of people you know/support/work with, might look like from a PTMF perspective.

We now turn to one of the most fundamental aspects of the Framework: the attempt to outline common or typical patterns in the ways people respond to the negative impacts of power.

Why do we need to identify general patterns in distress?

The PTMF draws on a wide range of ideas, approaches and critiques, and it is likely that at least some of them will be familiar to you already. Many existing therapy and self-help approaches are very consistent with the PTMF principles, which is why the PTMF *Overview* has appendices describing Open Dialogue, the Hearing Voices Network, narrative therapy and other approaches that already take a non-diagnostic perspective (appendices 2–14). The

PTMF can be seen as a very broad framework that accommodates and supports a range of specific models. It can also be used to identify gaps in these approaches, which very often arise out of not giving enough attention to the operation of power and the ideological meanings associated with it.

However, the PTMF argues that this kind of non-diagnostic thinking and practice should be the starting point for everyone, and not just a rare option that you may or may not be lucky enough to come across. In other words, although the PTMF can be used as it stands (for example, as suggested in the exercises in this book), we also want it to be more than just another way of constructing stories. As we've described in Chapter 3, it is intended to outline a whole new way of thinking that supports current examples of good practice, suggests new ones and offers a coherent replacement for the diagnostic model and the assumptions on which it is based.

A new conceptual framework needs to be broader than any particular approach if it is to take us beyond medicalisation and the *DSM* mindset. Unless it is based on revisiting and revising first principles, there will be two dangers: one, that non-diagnostic practice will remain a kind of 'fringe' activity because it is incompatible with the assumptions of the dominant model, and two, that 'new' approaches will simply turn out to be modified versions of the existing ones. We can see this in the enthusiasm for CBT, a type of therapy that has been rolled out across England through the Improving Access to Psychological Therapy (IAPT) programme for people with diagnoses of anxiety or depression. While CBT has useful aspects, in most versions it supports and maintains diagnostic thinking by playing down the role of social contexts and locating the problem and the solutions mainly within the individual.

In Chapter 2, we described how medicine is based on the process of identifying patterns in bodily problems, drawing on research into how the body works. These patterns are then matched to patients' complaints, resulting in a diagnosis. This has brought major advances in understanding and treating physical health problems over the last 150 years. We also saw that attempting to identify similar medical-type patterns in psychiatry has completely failed. The PTMF is our ongoing attempt to develop non-medical patterns, based on principles that are appropriate for emotional distress and troubled or troubling behaviour, rather than for understanding what may go wrong with our bodies. As we put it in the PTMF *Overview*:

> There are, and have always been, alternatives to diagnosis on an individual, one-to-one basis... What we have so far lacked is a supporting conceptual framework which works at a broader clustering and pattern-identification level. (p.2)

In other words, the PTMF is 'an over-arching structure for identifying patterns in emotional distress, unusual experiences and troubling behaviour, as an alternative to psychiatric diagnosis and classification' (Johnstone & Boyle, 2018b, p.2).

The previous chapters have looked at the elements of these patterns – power, threat, meaning and threat responses. This chapter looks at how we developed the patterns themselves.

The foundational pattern

Our starting point was to pull together the large amount of evidence into the origins of distress – or, in other words, the evidence for the roles of power, threat, meaning and threat responses, as summarised in the PTMF main document. This resulted in a very broad, overarching summary, which we have called the 'foundational pattern' (Figure 8.1), and which summarises much of the discussion so far (Johnstone & Boyle, 2018b, p.25). A written summary of the foundational pattern looks like this (Johnstone & Boyle, 2018b, p.24):

> Economic and social inequalities and ideological meanings which support the negative operation of power result in increased levels of insecurity, lack of cohesion, fear, mistrust, violence and conflict, prejudice, discrimination, and social and relational adversities across whole societies. This has implications for everyone, and particularly those with marginalised identities. It limits the ability of caregivers to provide children with secure early relationships, which is not only distressing in itself for the developing child but may compromise their capacity to manage the impact of future adversities. Adversities are correlated, such that their

Figure 8.1: The foundational power threat meaning pattern

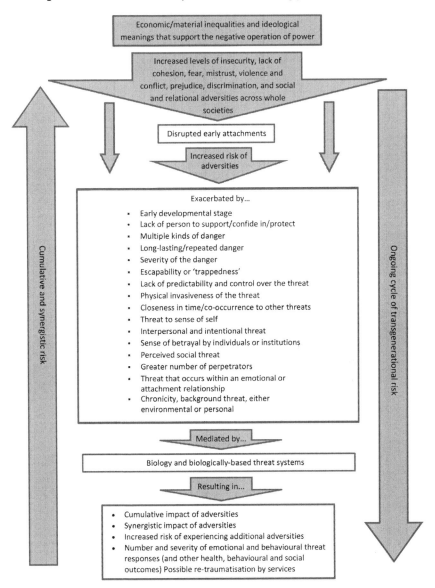

and the cycle may continue through transgenerational transmission of the impact of adversities

occurrence in a person's past and/or present life increases the likelihood of experiencing subsequent ones. Aspects such as intentional harm, betrayal, powerlessness, entrapment and unpredictability increase the impact of these adversities. This impact is both cumulative – the more the events, the worse the average outcome – and synergistic – the combined effect of more than one adversity is usually greater than the sum of their individual effects. Over time, the operation of complex interacting adversities results in a greatly increased likelihood of experiencing emotional distress and troubled or troubling behaviours. The form of these expressions of distress is shaped by available resources, social discourses, bodily capacities and the cultural environment, and their core function is to promote emotional, physical and social safety and survival. As adversities accumulate, the number and severity of these responses rise in tandem, along with other undesirable health, behavioural and social outcomes. In the absence of ameliorating factors or interventions, the cycle is then set up to continue through further generations.

Key characteristics of the foundational pattern

On the positive side, the foundational pattern describes trends, or increased risks, at the level of a whole population. It does not mean that particular individuals, families or groups who have experienced adversities are doomed to long-term distress, since a great deal depends on their own unique circumstances and meanings.

The factors that make threat harder to survive (listed under 'Exacerbated by' in Figure 8.1) were discussed in Chapter 5. As we've seen, research has shown that they make outcomes worse on average but, turned on their head, they can also make outcomes better. For example, if you have someone to confide in and keep you safe, as a general rule, you will find it easier to move on. Even if you don't have this kind of support at the time, it is never too late to seek it out in the form of someone who will listen, believe and help to protect you.

On the negative side, the foundational pattern shows very clearly that the overall impact of adversities is profound and ranges widely across many areas of life, and that if these impacts are not addressed, they may be transmitted down the generations, so that the destructive cycles continue to be played out in the lives of our children and grandchildren.

The pattern also reminds us that mental health and welfare services are often traumatising and re-traumatising in themselves, adding to, rather than reducing, the experience of distress, shame and exclusion.

The overall message is that the broad picture is absolutely clear and indisputable. We can see that all forms of adversity and distress are more common in social contexts of inequality and other forms of deprivation, discrimination, marginalisation and injustice. This evidence does not support the individualisation of distress, either medically or psychologically. Instead, it implies the need for action, primarily through social policy, at the earliest possible point, before the destructive and self-perpetuating cycles are set in motion.

The foundational pattern thus shows how urgently we need a change of model from 'This is a medical illness' to 'These are the understandable consequences of life circumstances'. However, it does not in itself answer the question posed earlier: How do we identify more specific patterns within this very broad picture, and what might they look like? Instead, it presents us with a new dilemma, which we have called the 'Everythings' problem: *Everything causes everything, everyone has experienced everything, and everyone suffers from everything.* In other words, all types of adverse experiences, all of which are common in the lives of people using services, seem to raise the risk for all types of distress (as well as for criminal and offending behaviour, physical health problems and many other undesirable outcomes) (Johnstone & Boyle, 2018b, p.13).

The 'Everythings' problem leads to what is described as 'co-morbidity' in psychiatric terms, as described in Chapter 2. This means that diagnostic categories overlap and most people in psychiatric services fit into several of them. Clearly, we need to think about patterns, or ways of grouping similar kinds of experience together, very differently if we are to resolve this.

This takes us on to a discussion of the principles of the general patterns that we have outlined within the broader foundational pattern.

The general patterns

We have described these patterns as provisional, or open to revision and development, for two reasons. First, they need more work to validate and flesh them out; in their current form, they are only a starting point. Second, it is in the nature of these patterns that they will evolve and change over time and across cultures. The reasons for this are explained below.

We have seen that the most damaging effect of diagnostic labels is to obscure people's personal meanings, conceal their stories and hide the link between their distress and the circumstances of their lives. In contrast, we wanted the PTMF patterns to serve the purposes of:

- showing that emotional distress and troubled or troubling behaviour are understandable responses to a person's history and circumstances

- restoring the link between distress and social injustice

- giving a central role to meaning-making, and

- helping to create validating narratives as an alternative to diagnoses.

We wanted them to be evidence-based in conventional terms, which is why they are based on a great deal of research (summarised in Appendix 1 of the main PTMF document) about ways in which people are likely to respond to certain kinds of power and threat. But we also wanted them to include the forms of evidence that are often discounted in what is called 'evidence-based practice'. In other words, rather than dismissing as 'anecdotal' what people say about their lives, we wanted to ensure the patterns value and draw on the personal testimony of human beings struggling to survive and make sense of their experiences and their lives.

The PTMF patterns involve a big leap in our thinking, and the rest of the chapter will be devoted to exploring this and spelling out its implications.

Characteristics of the general patterns

We have seen how patterns in medicine are based on descriptions of the various ways in which things can go wrong with our bodies.

But in talking about human thoughts, feelings and behaviours, we need to make a major shift towards very different kind of patterns, which are primarily shaped by our complex, meaning-based interactions with our physical, social and cultural environments. Of course, as discussed in the previous chapter, our bodies are inevitably involved at some level. But this is not the same as trying to understand distress in terms of patterns in biology. The PTMF patterns can be described as *embodied, meaning-based threat responses to the negative operation of power*. In other words, they draw on all the elements that we have discussed in earlier chapters – power, threat, meaning and threat responses – with meaning at their centre.

These are complex ideas, and we hope that the examples in the second half of the chapter will make them clearer. In the meantime, we outline some characteristics of the general patterns that follow from this central emphasis on meaning (a more detailed discussion about the characteristics of the general patterns can be found in the *Overview*, pages 42–46):

- The patterns are not based on simple cause–effect links between what happens to people and whether, or how, they might experience distress. This follows from the fact that everything is shaped by the meanings we create about the complex circumstances of our lives and the power resources available to us.

- As a result, the patterns are, and will always be, loose and overlapping, provisional and uncertain. There is no 'pattern for psychosis' or 'personality disorder', and nor do we expect a simple fit between one person's narrative and a specific wider pattern. This isn't a failure of the patterns. It is just how things are in the field of human emotional suffering, and it means that there is always hope for change.

- Having said this, there are certainly regularities, or common ways of responding to threat, that are rooted in our biology, our societies and our cultures. The patterns we describe here reflect these regularities.

- The patterns cut across 'normal' and 'abnormal' and 'mentally ill' and 'mentally well'. They apply to all of us, since we are all affected in some areas of our lives by the negative operation of power, we all experience threat, we all make meaning, and we all use threat responses.

• The patterns can be used to support the construction, or co-construction, of non-diagnostic narratives and stories about people's lives.

In summary, the general patterns represent what people *do* in the face of threat, and not 'disorders' that they *have*. The names of the general patterns reflect this. They talk about 'surviving' (which could also be phrased as 'managing' or 'coping with') certain life dilemmas, not about 'having' certain conditions.

The current list of general patterns is below – but it is important to note that it is provisional and is continually evolving. Summaries of all the general patterns can be found in the appendix to this book. The more detailed original versions, for those who are interested, can be read in the PTMF *Overview* (pp.47–73).

1. Identities.

2. Surviving rejection, entrapment and invalidation.

3. Surviving insecure attachments and adversities as a child/ young person.

4. Surviving separation and identity confusion.

5. Surviving defeat, entrapment, disconnection and loss.

6. Surviving social exclusions, shame and coercive power.

7. Surviving single threats.

The first general pattern, 'Identities', is our suggested starting point for thinking about the patterns. This is because our gender, ethnicity, sexual orientation, class, health and disability status, religion and so on shape everything else we experience. On average, people with more privilege and access to power in terms of these characteristics are exposed to fewer threats and have more resources to deal with them if they do occur. However, this generalisation does not apply in every individual case, since no one's life is guaranteed to be free from loss, trauma and adversity.

Moreover, most of us have several aspects to our identity – male and Black, perhaps, or female, gay and middle class, or White and disabled, and the benefits and disadvantages of each will intersect. And if we are diagnosed as 'mentally ill', this is likely to damage our identity, regardless of where we started in life.

Illustrating the use of the general patterns

This is a complex set of ideas to take on, and it may be helpful to provide some illustrations. Here is a shortened and slightly simplified version of the general pattern titled 'Surviving defeat, entrapment, disconnection and loss' (described in more detail in pages 63–66 of the *Overview*). Each general pattern starts with a brief summary, and then lists the typical power, threat, meaning and threat response aspects of that pattern. As you can see, this particular general pattern might describe people who have been given a diagnosis of depression, but equally it might describe other diagnoses (anxiety disorder, alcoholism and so on) or none at all. However, it is not a 'pattern for depression', and people who have been given a depression diagnosis might feel that they are better described by another pattern, or by a combination of patterns.

Surviving defeat, entrapment, disconnection and loss

This pattern describes people's attempts to survive feeling trapped in long-term situations of chronic stress, such as abusive relationships, or inescapable social environments such as poverty, loneliness, social exclusion, unemployment, refugee status and so on. Sometimes there were childhood experiences of loss, abuse, criticism, bullying and neglect as well. People using this survival pattern are likely to experience core feelings/meanings of defeat, entrapment, isolation and loneliness, hopelessness and loss. Poor physical health or pain and disability may add to the person's difficulties, and they may have a feeling of failure for not succeeding in line with social expectations. Threat responses may include low mood, exhaustion, giving up, self-blame, anxiety, or turning to alcohol and drugs.

This pattern of distress is more common in less powerful groups: for example, those who are female, low social class, older, and/or ethnic minority. These are the groups who are the most likely to suffer the consequences of high unemployment, low wages, poor work conditions and so forth. As with all the patterns, gender role expectations play a part. On the whole, women are more likely to be trapped in violent relationships or low-status jobs, along with carrying the main responsibility for childcare, while men are more likely to experience the trap of unemployment as a threat to their sense of identity and their place in the community.

At a broader level, the pattern shows how whole communities are impacted and fragmented by austerity, social inequality and injustice. This means that everyone, even those who are more affluent and protected, is likely to experience increased levels of feeling trapped and powerless, fear and distrust, isolation and loneliness, humiliation and shame and instability and insecurity.

The survival dilemma described in this pattern may be diagnosed as 'depression', 'anxiety disorder', 'post-natal depression' or alcoholism/substance abuse, along with other possibilities. It may also describe people who have never received a formal diagnosis.

It is not difficult to recognise people we know, or perhaps ourselves, in this description, and most therapists would be familiar with this kind of picture as well. The pattern draws on a great deal of published research (summarised in the main PTMF document (pp.340–342)), but the PTMF adds its own emphases to this existing knowledge by replacing a diagnosis with a broad narrative that makes sense of a person's reactions, making the links with wider social contexts and meanings, and showing that none of us, even the more fortunate, can isolate ourselves from the impacts of power. The potential benefits of sharing this pattern with someone who might previously have thought of themselves as 'having clinical depression' or 'having an anxiety disorder' or 'being an alcoholic' are:

- avoiding the stigmatising and disempowering messages of 'mental illness/disorder'

- encouraging them to reflect on possible meanings in their distress

- supporting the construction of their personal narrative by drawing on a general one

- recognising that their personal struggles are part of a common wider picture, and thus finding relief from guilt, shame, isolation and self-blame

- becoming aware of the limitations of medical solutions to their struggles

- suggesting ways forward that, as well as or instead of traditional interventions such as therapy, may include joining with others for self-help, solidarity and support, and perhaps finding new meanings and purposes in their distress and their lives.

From the perspective of the mental health system as a whole, we can see that the implications of viewing patients through a PTMF lens are wide-ranging. We could anticipate much less reliance on the usual responses of ever-changing diagnoses and drugs, in favour of a central role for all kinds of therapeutic relationships and social support. More broadly, the PTMF raises fundamental questions about the whole way our services are set up, including professional training, service commissioning and organisation, and the general responsibility of services to take a more active role in highlighting the links between social contexts and their human impacts, rather than simply labelling and sweeping up the casualties. (For more details on what this might look like in practice, see Chapter 11 of this book and Chapter 8 of the main PTMF document.)

From a societal perspective, we can see that recognition of this general pattern would be a major challenge to social and economic policies that are at the root of what are often called 'depression' or 'anxiety disorders', and to a narrow focus on interventions (both drugs and therapies) that locate the problem mainly within the individual. It also challenges the 'more of the same' message – more research, more doctors, more types of drug, more mental health services – that all political parties call for as a response to rising tides of distress. Research and services based on diagnostic principles are part of the problem, not part of the solution. When the link between threat and threat response, or between personal distress and social injustice, is highlighted through patterns of embodied, meaning-based threat responses to power, it cannot easily be hidden again.

We can illustrate these ideas further by looking at another general pattern. As a generalisation with many exceptions, women are socialised to turn distress inwards in the form of low mood, self-injury, self-starvation and so on, with the result that the pattern described above may often seem to reflect the dilemmas of women. The opposite applies to the pattern below, in which distress is more typically directed outwards in the form of aggression to others. While it is not a 'pattern for offenders', it describes many men who end up in the criminal justice system.

Surviving social exclusion, shame and coercive power

This describes the survival pattern of someone who is likely to have faced threat, discrimination, material deprivation and social exclusion in their early life, both inside and outside the family. This may have included an absent father, institutional care and homelessness. Parents and caregivers may have been struggling with their own histories of adversity, past and present, often by using drugs and alcohol. As a result of all this, the person's early relationships were often disrupted and insecure and they may have experienced significant traumas as a child and as an adult, including physical and sexual abuse, bullying, witnessing domestic violence, and harsh or humiliating parenting styles. Being sent to institutions like prison or psychiatric hospital may multiply the experience of threat. All of this may lead the person to experience core feelings/meanings of worthlessness, inferiority, powerlessness, shame, rejection and a sense of injustice. A variation of this pattern may arise in more privileged circumstances when young children are sent away to boarding school.

To cope with this, people often use survival strategies of cutting off from their own and others' emotions, maintaining emotional distance, distrusting others, remaining highly alert to threat, and sometimes defending against pain and humiliation by anger and violence. They may also suppress their feelings with drugs and alcohol. These responses are shaped, in men, by socialisation to direct their anger and pain outwards. 'Paranoia', or suspicious thoughts, is also common, and is linked especially in minority ethnic groups to actual experiences of discrimination, racism and exclusion.

These patterns are more likely to occur in economically unequal societies where people have to compete for jobs, resources and signs of achievement and material success. These pressures affect women and men slightly differently, due to gender role expectations. Men generally face greater pressure to compete, achieve and maintain social status, which means that, in an unequal society, disadvantaged men may face constant humiliating reminders of their failure to do this.

Along with 'paranoia', common diagnoses in men are 'anti-social personality disorder' or substance abuse, while women using these survival strategies are more likely to be labelled with 'borderline personality disorder' or 'bipolar disorder'. The pattern may also describe people who have never been formally diagnosed.

As we can see, the pattern attempts to go beyond describing the individual and to trace the roots back to societal structures and ideological messages. This pattern is strongly evidence-based – a mass of literature confirms that these power factors are typically (though not exclusively) found in the lives of men with criminal histories (Johnstone & Boyle, 2018a, pp.346–349).

The most likely institutional response to someone who fits this description is to diagnose them with 'anti-social personality disorder' and refer them to a specialist Offender Personality Disorder Service. The disadvantages of applying derogatory, individualising, context-free labels to behaviour that has complex psychosocial roots are obvious. Recognising that such services are largely dealing with people who can be described by this pattern would have implications not just for individual work but for staff supervision and training, the interventions that are offered, the way the service is organised, the language used to describe all of this, and so on. At a societal level, this general pattern promotes awareness of the social causal factors in criminal behaviour by making clear links with gender roles, social exclusion, domestic violence and economic inequality. The pattern demonstrates that intervention must happen not just at a one-to-one or staff or service level, but at a social policy level too – such as better early-years support, tackling unemployment and so on. This is a major challenge, but one the UK urgently needs to face, given its very high incarceration rates.

Ideological meanings in the general patterns

As we've seen, the PTMF places a strong emphasis on social norms and expectations, many of which are unquestioned, especially those that serve ideological purposes (see Chapters 4 and 6 of this book). Along with the work of many other people, our analysis suggests that socioeconomic structures influence the discourses and meanings that serve the interests of various kinds of power. A particular person's distress is likely to be increased in proportion to the extent to which they have been persuaded to take on these underlying assumptions. These discourses and ideological meanings inevitably shape the general patterns as well, as we will discuss below.

As a reminder, here are some assumptions that readers who grew up under the influence of Western norms and standards may have taken for granted. They may seem to describe the way the world just is, or should be. However, as we have already discussed, all of them could be – and in some cultures are, and historically have been – very different. Many of us expect ourselves to:

- separate from our family of origin in early adulthood

- set up our own nuclear family unit (two parents and two to three children)

- compete and achieve in line with social expectations about what kind of job, house, lifestyle, material possessions etc we should aspire to

- fit in with current standards about body size, shape and weight

- fit in with current expectations about gender roles

- see ourselves as essentially an individual rather than a member of a family or community group

- avoid 'irrational' experiences, such as hearing voices or holding beliefs that are unusual in Western culture

- bring up our children to fit in with the same standards

- constantly monitor our progress in all these areas and take a large degree of personal responsibility for achieving, or failing to achieve, them.

Let's unpick some of these, starting with the most obvious, and look at how they might contribute to the development of patterns of distress in Western or Westernised cultures.

As we saw in Chapter 4, we are all, especially women, expected to live up to very specific standards of weight and appearance – slim, fit, young, and so on. Increasingly, men are expected to live up to parallel standards of fitness, appearance and muscularity. It doesn't take much imagination to link this to the diet, magazine, beauty, fitness, food and cosmetic surgery industries. In an economic system based on profit, we all have to be persuaded to feel dissatisfied with our appearance in order for these businesses to make money out of us. Our minds and bodies become the battleground for these competing interests as we take on the message that happiness can only be found through achieving the latest ideal of physical perfection. The rising rates of anorexia and bulimia diagnoses are one result of this. But the epidemic of distress about eating is not inevitable, and nor is it driven by biological factors – research shows that 'eating disorders' flourish alongside industrialisation and the introduction of new standards of appearance through social media (see, for example, Ireland, 2009).

Not so long ago, there was a strand of thinking that encouraged us to make the links between body hatred, weight control and impossible standards of appearance (see, for example, Orbach, 1978). This is almost totally absent from mainstream therapies and treatment centres for people diagnosed with 'eating disorders', which have become a source of profit themselves in our increasingly privatised NHS (for an exception, see Holmes et al., 2017). The diagnostic model, even if supplemented by therapy, narrows the focus, with its message that the problem lies within the flawed individual. (For example, there are regular and misleading claims that genetic causes for 'eating disorders' have been found.) The PTMF general patterns widen the focus again, by showing that solutions will never be found simply at the level of one-to-one intervention. Not only do we all need to be made more aware of the ways in which our bodies are being exploited for profit; we also need to tackle the eating-disordered culture we live in. This might include, for example, stricter regulation of the food, diet, fashion and advertising industries.

Someone who recognises aspects of their individual story in one of the general patterns might find it helps them to move from feeling flawed and inadequate to justifiably angry at the way they have been exploited for profit, and determined to challenge the social messages and find their own ways to feel at ease in their bodies. As psychotherapist Susie Orbach puts it: 'We urgently need to curtail the commercial exploitation of the body… so that we and our children can enjoy our bodies, our appetites, our physicality' (Orbach, 2019). This applies to all of us, not just to those with diagnoses of eating disorders. Professor of psychology Paul Verhaeghe traces similar themes in his account of the shift away from a focus on social progress towards the project of the 'perfectible individual' who must work first on their minds (for example, through various therapies) and then on their bodies, encouraged by the relevant industries. As he notes, 'Meanwhile, a lot has changed in society without us noticing it: we're all too much focused on ourselves' (Verhaeghe, 2014, p.74).

Let's look at another example. Davina James-Hanman has spent 30 years working with survivors of domestic abuse. Usually, although not always, the perpetrators are men. She says the stories victims brought to refuges were so similar that:

> In the early days I used to have paranoid fantasies that there was some kind of secret abuser's handbook… Eventually I realised that there is, and it's not secret at all – it's called mainstream culture.

She describes meeting:

> … men who fear losing the power that comes with a rigid belief in traditional gender roles. Men who repackage 'girly' emotions such as insecurity, stress and fear as anger. Often they are not feeling anger at all but that's the only safe emotion

to feel because, if they stop believing in gender roles, their whole world starts to crumble. (Quoted in Usborne, 2019)

Domestic abuse perpetrated by men is known to be linked to rigid beliefs about gender roles (Herrero et al., 2017). Davina is clearly describing a wider, socially endorsed pattern underpinning the individual stories and shaping people's personal beliefs and actions. These gendered expectations can be traced back to the fundamental structures and beliefs of the majority of societies, past and present, in which men as a group have more power and status than women. The corresponding expectations on women to be more compliant, nurturing and home-based are also reflected in their personal beliefs and make it harder for women to challenge or even recognise domestic abuse and other forms of misuse of power (for an overview, see the main PTMF document, pages 116–128).

Davina also makes it clear that rising domestic abuse-related homicide rates are happening within a wider social context:

Well, did you think austerity was going to have no consequences? If anything, I'm surprised it has taken this long for the numbers to go up. Women are calling the police and they are not turning up. Or abusers are breaching bail and not being arrested. Legal aid has been cut… Women are turned away from refuges because they are full. Money for prevention work has all but dried up… this stuff makes a difference. (Quoted in Usborne, 2019)

We know that domestic abuse is more common in deprived communities. The wider impacts of power in communities fragmenting under socioeconomic pressures are replayed in our family relationships, as the general patterns show.

Here is another illustration of how the general patterns demonstrate the potentially crippling impact of ideological messages, sometimes in the absence of specific traumas or adversities and sometimes magnifying their effects. Each of the general patterns has examples of sub-patterns within it. They are not intended as a complete or definitive set, but examples that we hope to develop and add to. This is a sub-pattern of the general pattern 'Surviving defeat, entrapment, disconnection and loss' (Johnstone & Boyle, 2018b, p.65).

Surviving competitive defeat

Some people have a particularly strong drive towards achievement and success, derived from family and social expectations. If they feel they have not lived up to expectations, or it is not possible to sustain the drive, or they are suddenly faced with challenges or crises beyond their control, they may draw on a set of threat responses which we have called 'competitive defeat'. These consist of exhaustion and self-criticism with a sense of failure, shame and hopelessness, and at an extreme, suicidal feelings. Men may be more vulnerable to these messages and are the most at-risk group for suicide. Within this, economically disadvantaged men in mid-life have the highest suicide rates. This may be due to a combination of factors, including perceived failure to live up to masculine standards of success and control, in the context of relationship breakdown and socio-economic changes and pressures.

Someone struggling with this kind of crisis can be seen as having been persuaded to take on an unusually strong version of the values of competition and achievement. They may be outwardly very successful and, indeed, privileged, and may not have experienced obvious adversities. This may apply to some of the celebrities who report experiences of distress, even though their lives seem, from the outside, enviable. It may equally apply to working-class men who have, in effect, become victims of both austerity policies and the accompanying messages that it is their personal failure if they are no longer able to fulfil their expected gender roles (as we saw with Danny Whittaker's story in Chapter 6). Those same gender expectations may then make them feel unable to ask for help, for fear of being perceived as weak or inadequate. The likely consequence is being given a label such as 'depression'. The PTMF, in contrast, invites them to question the values that created the trap in the first place.

A variation on this pattern – a more general version of Danny's story – has been described in a comprehensive review of

'Why disadvantaged men in mid-life die by suicide', conducted by the Samaritans (Wyllie et al., 2012). Rather than simply attributing to 'mental health problems' the three-fold increase in the risk of suicide among this group, the report argued that:

> Masculinity – the way men are brought up to behave and the roles, attributes and behaviours that society expects of them – contributes to suicide in men. Men compare themselves against a masculine 'gold standard' which prizes power, control and invincibility. When men believe they are not meeting this standard, they feel a sense of shame and defeat. Having a job and being able to provide for your family is central to 'being a man', particularly for working class men. Masculinity is associated with control, but when men are depressed or in crisis, they can feel out of control. (Wyllie et al., 2012, p.1)

Further, the report placed this dilemma within a wider socioeconomic context:

> … these feelings are produced within a specific social, economic and cultural context… the shift from repressive prewar to liberal post-war culture; changes to the roles of men and women and to the structures of families; economic restructuring and the decline of traditionally male industries… The impact of these processes has not been uniform across society; they pose challenges in particular to the group of men currently in mid-life, and these challenges are exacerbated when men occupy low socio-economic positions… They have seen their jobs, relationships and identity blown apart. (Wyllie et al., 2012, p.3)

A sophisticated analysis of this kind makes it absolutely clear that recommendations need to go further than the usual calls for more mental health services. Accordingly, the report also highlights the need to: 'Assist men excluded from the labour market to (re) enter employment' and 'Ensure that suicide prevention strategies include explicit aims to reduce socio-economic inequalities' (Wyllie et al., 2012, p.3). A 2019 United Nations report emphasises that this perspective applies to suicide patterns worldwide:

> A human-rights approach to suicide goes beyond a focus on mental health concerns and places problems of inequality, homelessness, poverty, and discrimination at the heart of prevention strategies... Research suggests that... identifying depression in individuals and targeting them with biomedical interventions fails to reduce suicide risk... [and] obscures the need to address the structural factors that make lives unlivable. (Office of the High Commissioner for Human Rights, 2019)

As we have argued earlier, social norms and expectations are often based not on what human beings most need in order to thrive and meet their core needs but on what best suits our socioeconomic structures. The general patterns include and make explicit these ideological messages, often filtered through gender role expectations. In this way, people who have up to this point seen themselves as uniquely failing as individuals, and who have been silenced by the invalidation and shame of a diagnosis, can recognise themselves as part of a larger group that is collectively struggling to survive in impossible circumstances and meet social and ideologically driven expectations. Individual expressions of distress can be traced back to the power interests that, in contemporary neoliberal societies, too often value achievement above kindness, money above wellbeing and competition above community.

Further aspects of the general patterns: culture

As we noted in Chapters 2 and 6, a major problem for diagnostic systems is that expressions of distress change markedly across cultures. We saw that this presents problems for the medical perspective, given that, as we are members of the same species, diseases ought to look roughly the same wherever we live. We also saw that this is not a problem for a perspective in which meaning is central, since different cultural norms and understandings are bound to result in different ways of expressing and experiencing distress.

We can illustrate this with the example of 'spirit possession', which is sometimes seen as equivalent to the psychiatric term 'psychosis'. It is one of the unusual (from a Western perspective) expressions of distress that at the moment appears in the *DSM-*

IV appendix of 'Culture-bound syndromes' that are still awaiting assignment to a diagnostic category. One version of spirit possession, *cen*, is found in Northern Uganda, where civil war has resulted in widespread brutality and the abduction and forced recruitment of children as soldiers. Some young people report that their identity has been taken over by the evil ghost of a dead person. *Cen* has been found to be associated with high levels of war trauma and with abduction, and the spirit was often identified as someone the abducted child had been forced to kill.[1]

We can clearly see themes of power, threat, meaning and threat response in this description of a common pattern of distress from a particular part of the African continent. We can also see that it could be understood from a PTMF perspective without having to call it 'schizophrenia' or 'psychosis'.

We are not suggesting that the PTMF patterns should be exported in the same way as diagnostic thinking is being promoted through the Movement for Global Mental Health (Wainberg et al., 2017).[2] Collectivist cultures, where there is more emphasis on understanding distress within the contexts of extended family relationships, ties to village and social networks, relationship to house and land and so on would be likely to find much of the PTMF as alien as the diagnostic model (Bracken, 2002). Rather, we hope that the PTMF could stand alongside culturally very diverse and different approaches in such a way that each could support and learn from the other. That is why the PTMF includes causal factors that are omitted from most Western psychiatric and psychological models, such as the impact of colonialism, war, transgenerational trauma and loss of identity, culture, language, heritage and land. It also includes forms of healing such as culturally supported rituals and ceremonies, community narratives, values, faiths and spiritual beliefs that are less often considered within Westernised cultures to support the healing and integration of the social group.

The founder of a Māori mental health service that draws on creation legends to create new narratives with clients has commented:

---

1. For more about *cen* in Uganda, see https://neurocritic.blogspot.com/2013/01/spirit-possession-as-trauma-related.html

2. www.mhinnovation.net/organisations/movement-global-mental-health-mgmh

The PTMF supported our belief that there was a need to challenge the status quo… [It] has acted as a 'distant cousin' with more commonalities than differences. (Johnstone & Kopua, 2019, p.7)

Perspectives that are lost or marginalised in Westernised cultures have been retained in many indigenous ones, with the result that, as a 2018 New Zealand government enquiry into mental health and addiction concluded: 'We believe that many dimensions of the aspirations of Māori and Pacific peoples, especially the call for a holistic approach, point the way for all New Zealanders' (Government Enquiry into Mental Health and Addiction, 2018).[3] Being able to draw on frameworks that acknowledge the wisdom of these traditions, which often have a strong sense of connection to nature, the land and the animal kingdom, is particularly urgent at this time of environmental crisis.

We are now in a position to think about putting all this together in the form of a narrative or personal story. Before we do this, it may be useful to think a bit more about 'Identities'.

Exercise 7

Reflecting on identities

Someone's sense of identity shapes every other aspect of their life and the way they respond to threats and difficulties. It may be helpful to think about how various aspects of identity have influenced you, or the person you are working with or supporting. This is likely to include positive and helpful ways, such as feeling confident and being part of a group, as well as negative ways, such as being subjected to discrimination.

You may wish to think about ethnicity, class, age, gender, nationality, sexual orientation, religion, disability or being defined as 'mentally ill', or any other aspect of identity that is important to you or the person you are working with or supporting. As a starting

---

3. In 2019, Lucy Johnstone had an opportunity to explore the PTMF alongside members of a non-Western culture in New Zealand. See her blog at www.madintheuk. com/2019/02/crossing-cultures-with-the-power-threat-meaning-framework

point, it may be helpful to read through the summary of this general pattern, called 'Identities', which can be found in the Appendix to this book. Jot down anything that seems to apply so that it can be included in the emerging story.

If this exercise is in any way difficult or upsetting, we suggest you take a break and use the ideas and resources from Exercise 2 in Chapter 3.

Chapter 9
What is your story?

We can now see that narratives, or stories, lie at the heart of the PTMF, and that the simple answer to the question 'What do we do instead of diagnosing people?' is 'We listen to their stories.' Readers who have been applying the core PTMF questions to themselves, or supporting others to do so, will by now have some idea of the story that is emerging, and others may be able to get a sense of the process through the examples in this chapter.

As we have seen, the PTMF has implications for change at various levels beyond the individual, family or social group. However, in this chapter, personal stories will be our main focus. For simplicity, we have chosen examples from adults, although the principles apply equally to children, older adults, people with intellectual disabilities and other groups.[1] (Versions of the guided discussion in the PTMF *Overview* are being adapted for different groups and added to the main PTMF website as they are developed.[2])

We have argued that all societies develop certain narratives and discourses in order to preserve their structure and conventions, for better or for worse. The PTMF challenges the epistemic injustice of imposing one particularly powerful discourse, the diagnostic one, by making the framework's ideas freely available. Everyone in

1. The direct link is www.bps.org.uk/sites/www.bps.org.uk/files/Policy/Policy%20-%20 Files/PTM%20Overview.pdf

2. See www.bps.org.uk/power-threat-meaning-framework.

distress – which is all of us at times – has a life story, and every human being is highly skilled at making meanings and creating stories. Some versions of story-telling have found a place in therapy and mental health services, as described below, but the PTMF goes beyond these traditional forms of sense-making and gives equal value to art, poetry, dance, music and so on. It also acknowledges the many forms of narratives that may be healing at the level of the social group, especially in collectivist societies, through community or faith-based rituals, ceremonies, legends and so on. We are particularly pleased that the PTMF has been taken up by some peer groups of people who have used mental health services, who, independently from professional input, have been able to draw on its ideas to offer service users an alternative understanding to the diagnostic one (see Griffiths, 2019).

Developing a new narrative is not always easy and takes time. It does not instantly solve your difficulties or offer simple solutions. There will be aspects of your life that you cannot change – things that have happened in the past and situations that are beyond your control in the present, including the wider social factors that we have discussed throughout this book. The PTMF aims to hold a difficult balance between acknowledging the very real challenges and constraints in people's lives and, at the same time, believing in their capacity to make small changes, even if this is simply about modifying the meanings they create about themselves and their situations. As we phrase it in the PTMF main document:

> Human beings are active agents in their lives, both determined and determining beings, rather than objects acted upon by external forces. As human agents we both conform to the reality we encounter and seek to transform it. We do this through our capacity for meaning making, and for reflecting on and learning from our experiences. (Johnstone & Boyle, 2018a, p.47)

These are not easy positions to reconcile, which may be why some critics have accused the PTMF of viewing people as totally responsible for their fates, while others feel we have described people as helpless victims of wider social forces. Neither extreme is accurate. However, we do believe that creating a different narrative can be a deeply healing process, opening up new ways to 'exercise influence within inevitable psychosocial, biological and material constraints' (Johnstone & Boyle, 2018a, p.185).

Narratives in mental health and criminal justice settings

A version of a narrative, called a psychological formulation, is already used quite widely in UK mental health services. As described in Lucy Johnstone's book *A Straight Talking Introduction to Psychiatric Diagnosis* (2014, Chapter 7), formulation is a process in which a professional and a service user together create a theory or 'best guess' about the origins of the difficulties that have brought the person into mental health services. The formulation integrates the professional's clinical and research knowledge, such as evidence about the possible effects of trauma and adversity, with the service user's expertise in their own life. The formulation might take the form of a couple of paragraphs, or sometimes a diagram, that describe how the person's relationships, social circumstances and life events have come together to result in their current problems. The core of a formulation is working out the particular meaning of these events and contexts to the service user as an individual (or perhaps as a couple or family). Unlike diagnosis, this is not about making an expert judgement but about working closely with someone in order to develop a shared understanding that will evolve over time.

A formulation is not just based on problems and difficulties, or the things that are supposedly wrong with you, but draws attention to talents and strengths in surviving what are nearly always very challenging life situations. This has been described as 'a process of ongoing collaborative sense-making' (Harper & Moss, 2003). A good formulation helps us to escape from the 'brain or blame' trap (discussed in Chapter 4), offering a way out of the dilemma of 'You have a physical illness and therefore your distress is real and no one is to blame for it' versus 'Your difficulties are imaginary and/or your or someone else's fault, and you ought to pull yourself together.' The overall message of every formulation is that the person's experiences are understandable in context and represent their best attempt to survive difficult circumstances.

Formulations, like any other practice, can be carried out helpfully or less helpfully. The general pattern summaries discussed in the previous chapter can be seen as formulations constructed at a broader, clustering level. However, as we have seen, they take a wider lens than traditional psychological formulations, in that they make explicit links to ideological meanings and social injustice.

The PTMF gives examples of various other ways of creating narratives that are compatible with its principles. These include Open Dialogue, which is a way of promoting healing conversations in families where one person has been given a diagnosis of 'schizophrenia'; Narrative Therapy, which is an approach to opening up new meanings and stories in people's lives, and the Hearing Voices Network, a service-user led organisation for understanding and accepting the experience of voice-hearing.[3]

Formulation is practised by all clinical psychologists and some other professionals, and you may be able to request this approach, although some psychologists see it as an addition, not an alternative, to diagnosis. Open Dialogue and Narrative Therapy are less widely available. One of the aims of the PTMF is to make these and similar approaches the default model for mental health services, rather than scattered innovations that can only be accessed by postcode lottery. Future editions of the PTMF will expand on these examples to include people who see their breakdowns in terms of a spiritual crisis.[4]

The PTMF includes a list of criteria for avoiding the risks of using formulation, or any other narrative approach, in an individualising, context-free way (Johnstone & Boyle, 2018b, pp. 74–84). It suggests that we need to be aware of:

- the entrapping effect of the dominant narrative of psychiatric diagnosis and its wider context of assumptions from the natural sciences

- the contradictions inherent in combining psychiatric diagnostic narratives with psychosocial ones

- the role of discourses, especially those about gender, class, ethnicity and the medicalisation of mental distress, and how these discourses can permit others' meanings to be imposed

---

3. See appendices 9, 10 and 11 in the PTMF *Overview* (Johnstone & Boyle, 2018b).

4. See www.spiritualcrisisnetwork and www.emergingproud.com for more about this perspective on distress and unusual experiences.

- the impacts of coercive, legal, and economic power

- the nature and impact of power inequalities in psychiatric settings

- the prevalence of abuses of interpersonal power within relationships

- the role of ideological power, expressed through dominant narratives and assumptions about individualism, achievement, personal responsibility, gender roles, and so on

- the mediating role of biologically-based threat responses

- the importance of understanding the function and purpose of threat responses

- the role of social influences and power resources in shaping threat responses

- culture-specific meanings, belief systems and forms of expression

- self-help and social action along with, or instead of, professional intervention

- the importance of community narratives, values and spiritual beliefs, to support the healing and re-integration of the social group

- recognition of the varied, personal and provisional nature of all narratives and the need for sensitivity, artistry and respect in supporting their development and expression, whatever form they take

- the need to convey an overall message that is normalising, not pathologising (either medically or psychologically): 'You are experiencing an understandable and indeed adaptive reaction to threats and difficulties. Many others in the same circumstances have felt the same.'

The PTMF argues that narratives of all kinds will be more holistic, helpful, healing, empowering and evidence-based if they are based on recognition of the aspects listed above, even if not all these elements are present in each particular example. This will help to promote awareness about the origins of distress, both immediate and more distant; identify and demystify the influence of discourses and ideological meanings; restore the links between threats and threat responses; let go of narratives of stigma, shame and deficit; open up alternative ways of resolving emotional pain, and increase access to power and resources. As well as, or instead of, the more usual intervention options, such as psychiatric drugs and therapy, this process may involve drawing on or building on resources and strategies such as:

- secure early relationships

- supportive current partners, family and friends for practical and emotional support, protection, witnessing, validation

- managing overwhelming emotions by releasing/expressing/ processing feelings (e.g. writing, exercise, alternative therapies, creativity and the arts, compassion-focused approaches, mindfulness, meditation)

- self-care – for example, nutrition, exercise, rest, alternative therapies

- finding meaningful social roles and activities

- access to material resources/cultural capital/education and so on

- access to information/alternative perspectives

- positive/socially valued aspects of identity

- skills/abilities – intelligence, resourcefulness, determination, talents

- physical resources – strength, health, sporting abilities

- belief systems – faiths, values and so on

- culturally-supported community practices, rituals, ceremonies and interventions

- connections to the natural world

- supporting each other in campaigning, activism

- creating/finding new narratives/meanings/beliefs/values/ 'survivor missions'.

Some PTMF personal narratives

If you have tried out the exercises, you or the person you are working with or supporting will have an idea of how the personal story is shaping up. There is no final version of a story, and you may wish to return to it and update it, along with your changing reflections and circumstances.

Here are some examples of narratives developed by service users with the help of the PTMF. In several cases, the PTMF format has been adapted to suit individual preferences and settings. This is very much in keeping with our aim to offer the core questions as a flexible and adaptable structure for the construction of narratives of many different kinds. Please also be aware that narratives by current or former service users are likely to be based on particularly difficult situations and events. However, as we have emphasised throughout the book, even those who have been more fortunate are subject to the influence of power; we all experience distress at times and we all have a story to tell.

Emma's story

Emma is a social worker who has also used services. Partly through having had good support from a mental health team, she has done a lot of thinking about her story already. Here, written from a position some way along in her journey, she uses the PTMF core questions as a self-help reflection tool (this is a slightly revised version – the original can be read in Randall et al., 2020).

'What has happened to you?' (How is power operating in your life?)

My late childhood and early adolescence took place against a background of a general 'chaos' and threat, punctuated by incidents of aggression, often fuelled by alcohol. I didn't feel safe, and this was frequently ignored, dismissed or seeming not to be heard or taken in by members of my extended family, teachers, the parents of friends. I think I gradually lost trust in how I experienced the world around me. 'I must be wrong.' Maybe internal family discourses that 'Adults know better than children', broader narratives surrounding gender – 'Girls should be nice', 'Being quiet and compliant is desirable and good' and, in my growing-up world, a religious (Roman Catholic) narrative – intensified these things. Such narratives hold intense power to silence, trivialise or intimidate. Another commonly held attitude at the time was that both addiction and inter-familial violence were 'family matters'. This ideology shored up the secrecy and created another barrier to speaking out. It meant that when I did ask for help, aged 14, by calling the police in the middle of an aggressive dispute, my story was brushed aside by the (male) police officer as exaggeration.

There were social and economic 'threats' too. Not unusually, my mum had few material resources available to only her, and this meant that escaping from a relentlessly threatening situation felt impossible. When we did leave, unstable and inconsistent housing and the fragile sense of safety that brings, maintained this sense of threat.

I think the cumulative effect of this was that when other things that were equally serious but different in nature occurred at a later time, I did not consider asking for help to be an option. So as often happens, the impact of power in one area left me vulnerable and alone in another.

'How did it affect you?' (What kind of threats does this pose?)

Domestic abuse often creates a range of threats, some of which are more visible than others. Bodily and relational threats, isolation from social networks, lack of financial and material resources and separation from sources of potential support in the community. Shame fuels secrecy. I think a big threat for me involved simply not feeling safe, either physically or psychologically, and therefore feeling very easily overwhelmed in situations which otherwise I might have managed. I had already used up my resources at home and they didn't get replenished very often. This meant that, although school offered a degree of safety and predictability (I loved learning), 'fun' and playfulness felt pointless and navigating friendships was difficult (how can you invite someone home when you are unsure what you will be bringing them home to?). I was aware from a young age of how alcoholism was perceived and that having an alcoholic parent made me different and somehow 'less than'. I think I tried to compensate for this with relentless striving – to achieve academically, to please, and to be as 'clean' and 'ordered' as possible.

So domestic abuse and the impact of addiction were key threats, 'witnessing' aggression, but also directly being the target of it (I don't like the term 'witnessing' domestic abuse being applied to children. They are in it and experience it.) Being left in unsafe situations, with unsafe people, being given a level of responsibility too much for the stage of development I was at. I was acutely aware from a young age of existing within intergenerational patterns of addiction. And in trying desperately to resist what seemed like an inevitable fate by maintaining 'control', I fell into the compulsivity of anorexia. The way in which the anorexic state of mind takes the person over and divorces them from their sense of self means that it can be conceptualised as both a threat and a threat response. Anorexia left me confused about who I believed myself to be, and mirrored the confusion I felt about the validity of my needs and the reasonableness of taking up space in the world. It was augmented (but not caused by) the subtle and ever-present scrutiny that comes with living in a woman's body in a world seeking to create dissatisfaction in all of us.

'What sense did you make of it?' (What is the meaning of these experiences to you?)

Unsurprisingly, the meaning I took from my experiences was fairly bleak. Mainly a sense of difference, inadequacy, 'unlikeable-ness'. This was often focused on my body but it extended to my core sense of self. 'I am not okay as I am but maybe if I try hard enough, it will compensate for this.'

I also developed a strong sense of responsibility. 'I'm responsible'; 'I have to hold things together or everything will fall apart.' I think until beginning to discover feminist literature and meeting others who unapologetically took up space, I felt that I must exist solely to meet others' needs and had little sense of being seen, valid or deserving of space, a voice, care. This was mirrored by the 'anorexic' denial of needs which functioned to cut me off from all feelings and manage the sense of overwhelm I often experienced. I became, sometimes quite literally, frozen.

'What did you have to do to survive?' (What kinds of threat response are you using?)

My major threat response described in the Framework was, until recently, that of restricted eating, coupled with striving, and strategies such as overwork and perfectionism. Restrictive patterns around food make sense as a means of gaining a sense of control and 'coping' whilst also functioning to disconnect from some of the more intrusive symptoms of trauma. Once I regained some control back from restrictive patterns around food and regaining weight, other threat responses became more prominent, mainly anxiety-based responses such as flight/freeze in response to reminders of earlier experiences, nightmares and compulsions aimed at appeasing intrusive thoughts and probably also squashing down feelings. I have found that the PTMF can help to make sense of shifts in particular 'symptoms' or behaviour patterns. If the impact of the core threat is not addressed, it makes sense that symptoms will shift and change as a person seeks to manage this in whatever way feels most accessible to them at the time. I think another (less conscious) control strategy was to keep certain areas of my life quite separate from others as a way of coping.

Another key strategy involved trying to desperately keep the people I depended on as emotionally 'together' as possible by being compliant, appeasing, trying to anticipate and meet their needs, trying to not get in the way or make things more difficult – and therefore automatically dismissing what I might feel, need or want because it was too much and in any case, there was no space for this. Again, this left me vulnerable. Looking back, I was painfully compliant, terrified of doing something 'wrong' and working very hard to please and appease the adults around me. This probably set me up for limited friendships with peers because it took a great deal of energy and – being honest – I wasn't very 'fun'.

What are your strengths? (What access to power resources do you have?)

In spite of the difficulty, there were some really quite powerful positive influences in my life, and I'd like to think that they served as a protective or mitigating factor. I had a warm relationship with my grandmother and a very kind, 'comfortable', fun aunt. What this meant was that my sibling and I had a refuge away from the 'chaos', and in this warm environment were able to feel safe and relaxed enough to have fun, to play, to develop our interests. I think this was vital and provided an island of stability from which to build.

From a young age, I read. In some ways this was quite obsessive because at quite a young age it became a soothing strategy. It also helped me to learn. The striving pattern gave me the motivation to work hard and complete my education to postgraduate level. This opened up opportunities and new ways of thinking and seeing the world. I realised that there were other, more compassionate, hopeful ways of viewing the world. I also (very importantly) had a sister who, particularly as we grew older, was a source of solidarity and mutual validation: 'This isn't right, is it'; 'This doesn't happen at so and so's house'; 'I felt sad when that happened too.'

The Framework mentions the phenomenon of 're-victimisation', including by mental health services. I consider myself fortunate to have largely had an experience of services (and therapy) that has been kind, restorative and has offered a framework for something new. I have for some time worked in mental health services, and I want to do all I can to help services and practitioners to be trauma informed, and to break down the 'us and them' attitude that can persist within services. We are all human.

Emma adds a reflection on the importance of some key relationships on her path to healing.

And what about the way out...?
When thinking about changing or revising these (now largely unhelpful) survival strategies, one huge thing for me has been a relationship with someone who is kind and has remained kind and continued to see 'me', even after knowing the 'really bad stuff'. Contact with services who have on the whole been compassionate, understanding and really, really tried to help has also been important. Over the last couple of years, I've felt genuinely listened to, psychologists have taken the time to map out patterns with me, helped me to tolerate the risk of beginning to change those, and have validated that it is OK to need help with that process. I think there was something powerful about my partner, therapist and the service I attended all being on the same page. Fighting that relentless 'anorexic mindset' can feel so confusing. Having someone bravely say 'Yes, they are right' when I was raging against having to eat yet another 'unnecessary' meal was actually really helpful. Someone I trusted told me, 'This is what you need to do, and you can do it,' and I replayed that in my mind over and over as an anchor. I couldn't always verbalise things, so I wrote sentences and handed them over,

drew doodles, and wrote blog posts – all perhaps attempts to find my voice and put words to too big things.

A while ago, I wrote myself a note that, 'Whatever happens, the bravest thing I can do is to step away from the critical, dismissive, punishing patterns as much as I can each day.' It is scary. Still. But it was a commitment. It helped me to take what are actually quite significant risks to me, even though they may not look like that to others. My motto for a while was 'Be more "reckless" and less rigid'. I am trying out ways of attending to myself, trying to carve out moments of calm, reminding myself that, as a result of my 'back story', I might need different things to others sometimes.

Survival strategies can turn on you and trap you and that is what restrictive and controlling patterns do. 'Anorexia' was my way of surviving horrible things, but it became tangled into almost every aspect of my life and sense of self. It began as a form of resistance to and a barrier against oppression but then I found myself in a position of needing to resist it and finding allies around me, and within me, to help me to do that. So when I think about power, I also think about resistance. Resistance, for me, involves risking kindness towards myself and others, risking allowing more, both physically and psychologically. The kindness of many other people – my husband, friends, services and strangers on the internet – has been a huge part of this beginning to shift. It's a slow chipping away but the more of those kind interactions I have, the more my cynical, jaded, terrified worldview is challenged.

Finally, Emma testifies to healing power of narrative.

I think the final piece of resistance for me involves the power of finally telling my story. Telling it, validating it, daring to speak it, daring to use the words, daring to sit in a room and look at it, taking risk after risk. I hope I am finding a space to tell mine. Slowly, haltingly, but telling it. In words and pictures and silences. 'Liberation is always in part a storytelling process: breaking stories breaking silences, making new stories. A free person tells her own story. A valued person lives in a society in which her story has a place' (Solnit, 2017, cited in Randall et al., 2020, p.152).

We have reproduced Emma's story at some length, with her generous permission, because it illustrates the PTMF themes so well. We can see the overlapping themes highlighted by the core questions and the clear links between the power-based threats and the threat responses. Emma could have met the criteria for various diagnostic labels at different times, but the PTMF shows how all of her 'symptoms' were in fact survival strategies that helped to create a degree of safety in her unsafe world, even if the cost to her was high. She identifies the less obvious threats, such as invalidation, silencing and loss of trust, and the less obvious threat responses, such as perfectionism, striving, compliance, self-surveillance and pleasing others. She also shows that the private hell enacted behind the walls of her family home was an echo of wider abuses of power and ideological messages. This included women's and men's gender-role expectations, lack of material resources, and societal discourses of shame, secrecy and denial. This in turn led to isolation in her community and betrayal by organisations and institutions (her school, the police) that should have stepped in to protect her. Finally, she shows the central importance of caring relationships, both personal and professional, within which her story could be reconstructed and heard.

Using the PTMF in peer groups

Another way of using the PTMF narrative structure is in peer groups, as the Portsmouth-based SHIFT (Self Help Inspiring Forward Thinking) recovery group has been doing (SHIFT Recovery Community, 2020). They decided to meet weekly to read and discuss sections of the PTMF Overview document and apply the ideas to their own lives. The sessions began with a check-in to see how each person was feeling, and finished in the same way, to ensure the safety of the group. Facilitation of the group was shared. Together the group worked through the chapters, with one person reading out loud, stopping at any time to engage in group discussion, unpick the language and concepts and share thoughts and experiences. Each person completed the template diagram from the guided discussion in the PTMF *Overview* (Appendix 1, p.91) and shared their life stories with the others. Over time, they found:

> We began to develop a new perspective: rather than seeing ourselves as abnormal and disordered – which had left us

feeling hopeless and blaming ourselves for our difficulties – we began to see our 'symptoms' as understandable reactions to abnormal and threatening life circumstances… This was a very therapeutic process as we felt our experiences were recognised, validated and understood and we began to feel more hopeful about the future.

Here is how one person found the process:

Anonymous male, aged 26

I grew up as an only child to a single parent, within a family culture unconsciously based on what I now understand to be maladaptive behaviours and co-dependency. Personal traumas – for example, poverty, abusive partners, family death, physical health, unsafe living environments and substance misuse – were to be treated with unfaltering denial and a stiff upper lip was to be maintained. The family normalised this chaotic environment and was oblivious to any harm it caused. As a result, I endured childhood neglect. This experience carried on throughout my time at school, where I struggled to meet social and academic expectations. After I had finished my education, I became reclusive and struggled to cope with life's demands. I began to self-medicate with drugs and alcohol in order to engage socially. This ultimately led me to SHIFT after a mental breakdown.

I was diagnosed with dyslexia at the age of 18 and ADHD at the age of 22 and was prescribed medication for anxiety and depression between the ages of 19 and 25. After learning about the PTMF, I realised that my underlying traumas had been completely ignored by professionals during this period. There was such poor communication between different services that I ended up playing the role of 'messenger' between them. I found this overwhelming and it was frustrating that all I seemed to be offered was more diagnoses and medications. As I waited for referrals to different services and was trying to manage the side effects of the medication I had been prescribed, I began self-medicating with drugs and alcohol.

The PTMF has increased my self-awareness and accelerated my personal development. I now understand that there is nothing intrinsically 'wrong' with me, and that, instead, my symptoms are coping mechanisms to help me deal with past trauma. Instead of being offered a diagnosis of ADHD, I could have been offered an opportunity to construct my own personal narrative. This would have helped me become aware much sooner that, because of my estranged relationship with my father and because my mother was emotionally absent, I had not had any secure early relationships. This, combined with the kinds of threatening situations I've mentioned, led me to developing threat responses in order to survive. Instead of understanding myself as being a person with ADHD, I could have begun to understand that I had developed threat responses as a way of regulating overwhelming feelings and as a way of finding meaning and purpose in life.

I also believe that if I had been offered the opportunity to share my life story with others, as we did in the SHIFT PTMF group, that I would not have experienced the distress and confusion I felt when playing messenger between the different services. I could have, instead, been supported by the services to find the right support for me in understanding myself and the world I live in. From there I could have begun to understand how and why I perceived threat, and learnt how to manage and overcome these threat responses.

A peer group in York has used the PTMF in a similar way (Griffiths, 2019). The core questions were presented on a flipchart for the whole group to view, based on the guided discussion structure in the PTMF *Overview*. One peer member presented the session, and another facilitated the discussion. Each question was carefully and sensitively explored in turn. This provided a foundation from which group members could begin to revisit events in their lives. They shared their personal experiences of childhood trauma and other kinds of adversity and reflected on how this had impacted on them throughout their life. In the words of the facilitator, Amanda:

We found that the Framework is applicable to many forms of adversity, even where there is no history of overt trauma, such as sudden unemployment or homelessness, stigma and discrimination, or even adapting to life-changing circumstances such as health difficulties etc. They also found that the Framework can be revised to fit the individual's uniquely personal narrative, offering an alternative understanding to the biological ones given to many group members. Members were able to use the supportive peer-led environment to develop their narratives without professional support. Through sharing and reflecting on their experiences, they developed insight into how disempowerment, threats to autonomy, and many other misuses of power had impacted negatively on their lives and often continued to play out in the present. They welcomed the description of their reactions as normal human responses to challenging and traumatic events and circumstances. These threat responses had often been unwittingly reinforced by services which had pathologised these responses even where there was a clear history of adversity.

The effect on the group members was powerful:

We found that sharing experiences… is an emotive and thought-provoking way to connect with others… and this may be the first time that the narrative and pain have truly been heard… This takes us from being isolated and lonely individuals to being part of a wider community of equals. (Griffiths, 2019, p.13)

This is how Amanda summarised her own story, rewritten through a PTMF perspective as an alternative to the diagnosis of 'borderline personality disorder'.

What is my story?

Numerous adverse childhood experiences led to subsequent traumatic life-changing events throughout my life. Constant repetitive cycles of coercion, powerlessness and multiple forms of abuse are affecting every aspect of my life, thus impacting on my physical, emotional and psychological wellbeing. My energy levels are depleted from being consistently broken and distressed by an authoritarian mental health system that prejudicially recast my pain and suffering when I needed compassionate, trauma-informed provision. As a consequence, I am dispirited and struggle to trust others. However, despite the ongoing clinical dispute with statutory mental health services, independent specialists have recognised the complex post-traumatic stress I endured. My relationships with my family and my peers are protective factors that motivate me to find the strength to utilise my experiences to self-educate and self-advocate. I also campaign for trauma-informed and trauma-specific services, and improved mental health provision for other survivors. (Griffiths, 2019, p.12)

Supporting people to construct PTMF narratives

Readers who use the PTMF to support others in constructing their stories will be drawing on what Alec Grant, a retired mental health nurse and academic, has called 'narrative competence… the capacity for human beings to deeply absorb, interpret and appropriately respond to the stories of others' (Grant, 2015, p.52). Arguably, this is the core skill required of everyone in what might broadly be called the helping professions, whether they work in statutory or voluntary services. It goes beyond (although may include) formal therapy and requires us to bear witness to people's suffering and stand alongside them in their search for validation and justice. Below are some examples.

Natalie Collins, whom we met in Chapter 4, works with survivors of domestic abuse and believes that the PTMF 'can change lives and open up the possibility to move away from the pathologisation of people, to a new space… where someone's distress can be validated, and they can be cared for in ways that do not ignore or minimise other people's choices, structural inequality, or difficult circumstances' (personal communication; see also Collins, 2019). She says:

The Own My Life course sees women as the experts in their own lives. Instead of viewing them as 'psychologically abnormal', it assumes that their reactions are understandable as a way of coping with the abuser's behaviour. He is the problem, not her. As I was developing the course, I was hugely excited to discover the PTMF, not only because it gave a robust academic rationale to the core values of the course, but because it gave me a structure to further help women to make sense of their lives. This led me to create a 13-minute video which explains the framework in simple terms, for practitioners and the women they support.

The course is based on a train-the-trainer model, with practitioners learning how to facilitate it with women who have been subjected to abuse. As a result of incorporating the PTMF, domestic abuse workers have reported that they now ask different questions of women who need refuge accommodation. One practitioner told the story of a woman who had cut her arm very severely and was rushed to hospital, where she was seen as acutely mentally ill. However, the PTMF perspective helped the staff to understand that she was actually trying to remove a tracking device which her abusive partner had said he had injected into her arm while she was asleep. His abusive tactics caused her to believe him.

Similarly, after watching and discussing the PTMF video, women who have been subjected to abuse report that they feel more able to understand why they have reacted in the ways they have and are less likely to blame themselves or feel guilty. (Personal communication)

Three prison staff used the PTMF to structure a group for men labelled with 'personality disorder' who were serving life or indeterminate sentences (Reis et al., 2019). The focus was 'Surviving Prison' and the staff felt that, given the inevitable operation of power and threat in this setting, the core PTMF questions were likely to be particularly appropriate. Interestingly, the answers mapped closely onto the various types of power identified in the PTMF. For example, the men reported experiencing coercive power (physical threat, violence and so on) and ideological power (racial attacks, being silenced), leading them to use various threat/ survival responses (withdrawing, portraying oneself as dangerous and ruthless, appeasing others, becoming a bully; excessive use of the prison gym, drugs). The men then shared their individual narratives of prison survival with the group in whatever format they preferred – written, diagrammatic or verbal.

Feedback from the group members and the facilitators was very positive:

> The group gave us a platform to speak about things that I have not had the opportunity to speak about previously… the framework allowed individuals to acknowledge and own their challenging behaviour, whilst putting it into context… The open-ended questions provided by the framework seemed to allow group members to speak openly about their experiences… and allowed meaning-making by the group as a whole, which felt like a rich and useful process. (Reis et al., 2019)

Clinical psychologist Anjula Gupta works in adult mental health services. She describes how the PTMF has encouraged a broader understanding of the experiences of Black and Asian minority ethnic (BAME) service users:

> Mental health services in western societies have been developed according to a dominant social construct of distress as a sign of a mental health problem (or illness/disorder) rather than a natural response to unnatural or threatening experiences. The PTMF has been used by two clinical psychologists in training open to all multidisciplinary teams in the NHS trust. The training aimed to demonstrate how the PTMF could be used to understand the stories of BAME service users who have unusual experiences that may be labelled as schizophrenia or psychosis. It focused on the relationship between a wider definition of trauma (discrimination, racism, poverty) and unusual experiences and the importance of providing a curious and safe space to hear stories of discrimination and link this to the distress presented in services. Evaluation of this training revealed that the PTMF helped people to understand how power affects service users, providing them with questions and conversations they could have with people that they hadn't had before. Participants shared experiences of using this learning in supervision and with service users. (Personal communication)

Drawing on the general patterns
Drawing on the general patterns as a professional

Some professionals have found the general patterns helpful in thinking about common themes in their clients' difficulties. Two psychologists working with a specialist autistic spectrum condition and intellectual disability service have found that their clients' lives frequently resonate with one of the sub-patterns of the general pattern 'Surviving defeat, entrapment, disconnection and loss'. The sub-pattern is called 'Surviving exclusion and competitive defeat as non-typical or non-conforming.' This is an extract from it (Johnstone & Boyle, 2018b, p.65):

The narrower the range of acceptable ways of being, and the more individualistic and competitive the social norms, the harder it is for people who are non-typical in various ways to find a social role and place for themselves and the more likely they are to experience feelings of failure, inadequacy, shame and exclusion.

The clinicians commented:

We have used this pattern to inform formulations that position mental health as secondary to experiences of social inequality and exclusion: for example, in letters to Job Centres requesting reasonable adjustments to job search procedures. (Flynn & Polak, 2019)

They also found that the general pattern 'Surviving disrupted attachments and adversities as a child/young person' was helpful in developing shared understandings with some clients, because it 'explicitly broadens... formulation socially and intergenerationally' (Flynn & Polak, 2019).

Drawing on the general patterns as a service user

Matt is a mental health nurse who was given a diagnosis of 'schizophrenia' as a young man and spent several years in the mental health system, where he was seen as unlikely to recover. Over time and with the right support, he was able to rebuild his life and leave his label behind. He had already done a lot of thinking about his personal story when he came across the PTMF, but he felt that this perspective gave him some important extra insights, and encouraged him to reveal, for the first time, traumatic events that had remained hidden. In reflecting on his encounter with the PTMF, he said:

It was emancipating to consider the pattern of 'Surviving defeat, entrapment, disconnection and loss', which offered me permission to tell the parts of the story that have never been told. This had a profound impact on me... the difference in seeing this pattern is that my story has been retold, this time including core abuses and negative operations of power that underpin years of deep hopelessness, loneliness and entrapment... Telling the previously untold stories of abuse and then the gradual healing of the shame, has eroded layers of negative power in my life.

I am not sure I could have perceived myself ever looking powerfully back at the abuse without the opportunity to hear my story, not through a problem-saturated depiction of me as deserving what happened, but through understanding of common and survivor shared reactions to people misusing their position and power to enact harm on me and others who have suffered in similar ways... This has been a profound process of escaping from entrapment towards hope and companionship. (Personal communication)[5]

Reflections on narratives as an alternative to psychiatric diagnosis

One of the comments people regularly make about the PTMF is that it is 'basically common sense – you find out what's happened in people's lives and start from there'. They have a point – but in the face of a very powerful, ideologically driven counter-narrative like the diagnostic one, it is sometimes necessary to go a long way round (200,000 words, in the case of the main PTMF document) to establish, or re-establish, common sense. The PTMF achieves this by demonstrating:

1. that the narrative approach as a whole is a valid and workable alternative to the diagnostic one

2. that personal/family/group narratives can be shown to draw from wider cultural narratives

3. that the broad shape of these cultural narratives or general patterns can be supported by current evidence, in its conventional forms

4. that the general patterns can also support and draw from forms of evidence that are often discounted. This includes personal testimony (often dismissed as 'anecdotal evidence')

---

5. A talk by Matt can be seen at www.youtube.com/watch?v=lXR7g8EWV04

– in other words, what people actually say about their thoughts, feelings, lives, relationships, experiences and meanings.

In these ways, the PTMF goes beyond the current use of formulation and allows us to value narratives that may not be evidence-based in a conventional sense, as well as those that are. When we are making sense of our suffering, we may sometimes want to think beyond literal or historical 'truth' in the sense in which it is usually understood in Western thought. A different kind of test may sometimes be more relevant, such as: Does the narrative make sense from the perspective of the person? Does it offer relief, does it *feel* true at a personal level? As one client put it, when offered a particular account of her difficulties: 'It all just made sense. I got it because it was true. It seemed true to me anyway' (quoted in Johnstone & Boyle, 2018a, p.253).[6]

The notion of 'narrative truth', as opposed to historical truth, is important here (Spence, 1982). This allows us to work respectfully within whatever frame of reference is meaningful to the person/social group, however unusual it may be, and to value the resulting narrative according to whether it seems to 'fit' in a way that 'makes change conceivable and attainable'. Clearly, we can never know for certain whether a hostile voice really represents someone's abusive parent. Nor are Maori creation stories (as described in the previous chapter) about a sky father and earth mother compatible with scientific evidence about the origins of the universe. But in both cases, these kinds of meanings have been shown to have narrative truth for particular groups or communities, and to offer healing ways forward.

As we have said, it is important to acknowledge that distancing yourself from mainstream ideas and assumptions and constructing new narratives, if that is your choice, is not a quick, easy or complete solution. It may be very hard to free oneself from the internalised stigma of diagnosis. Long-standing forms of

---

6. Articles, blogs and resources about the experience of hearing voices can be found at www.intervoiceonline.org. A clinic that uses Māori creation stories to heal distress is described at www.stuff.co.nz/national/102115864/in-narrative-therapy-mori-creation-stories-are-being-used-to-heal

distress may not disappear, although it may be possible to find ways of living alongside them. Healing from some of the consequences of diagnosis – such as the effects of psychiatric drugs – may take months or years, or perhaps never be complete. Struggles with finances, housing, low-paid employment and so on may continue to dominate daily life. And caution is needed about misuse of the idea of narrative itself. Some service users have protested at the pressure to produce an acceptable 'recovery story' with a happy ending, while fundamental social and economic structures remain unchanged (Costa et al., 2012).

Having said all this, there is a growing body of testimony about how narrative approaches of all kinds can support a process of 'reclaiming our experience in order to take back authorship of our own stories' (Dillon & May, 2003, p.16) and thus promote 'the restorative power of truth-telling' (Herman, 2001, p.181). As these ideas spread, they may contribute to a wider process through which, 'When people share their stories without others imposing meanings on them, this creates social change' (Mead & Filson, 2016, p.109). We hope the PTMF makes a contribution to that process.

The next chapter will briefly describe some of the other ways in which the PTMF ideas are being used.

Exercise 8

What is my story?

If you or the person you are working with or supporting have tried out the exercises so far, you will have a good idea about what the story looks like. There is no prescribed way of telling it.[7] Emma, in the example in this chapter, did not feel the need to write a summary of the Power, Threat, Meaning, Threat Responses and Strengths themes. Amanda did want to pull her responses together into a final

---

7. The following are some examples of creating narratives through art: *Diary Drawings: Mental illness and me*, by Bobby Baker with Dora Whittuck, published by Profile Books (2010); *Putting Myself in the Frame: Drawing hope from art therapy*, by Sally Fox (2015), £7.00 plus £2.00 p&p from sally.fox@btinternet.com, and *A Tough Nut to Crack: Poems and essays on psychiatric care*, by Jo McFarlane (2017), £8.00 plus £2.00 p&p from edinburghjo@yahoo.co.uk

narrative. Matt went a bit further and found a sense of reassurance by comparing his story with one of the general patterns. Any of these approaches is fine, or you can use it any other way that seems helpful to you. Similarly, you or the person you are supporting might want to write the story down, as these three people did, or keep it in a diagrammatic form, or tell it to someone else, as some of the peer and prison group members did. Another option is to use the template in the online guided discussion as a summary (you'll find this at **www.bps.org.uk/sites/www.bps.org.uk/files/Policy/ Policy%20-%20Files/PTM%20Guided%20Discussion.pdf**). There is no right or wrong way.

A simplified version of the main general patterns can be found in the appendix to this book. If you decide to look at them as part of constructing a story, please remember:

- They are not simple replacements for particular psychiatric diagnoses. They cut across diagnoses, and also include people with no diagnosis at all.

- Often there is no neat fit between a particular person and a particular general pattern. Many people will recognise parts of their story in several patterns.

- The responses they describe are on a spectrum. The effects of power and threat on a particular person depend on many factors that make the impact either worse or better. Some people will have much milder difficulties; others will have greater struggles.

- The patterns will be amended and changed over time as more evidence emerges. In particular, we know less about typical patterns in non-Western cultures and settings, in the UK and across the world.

Having said all this, the general patterns may prompt reflections about additional aspects of the story and may help to show you that you are not alone in your experiences, feelings and reactions.

Stories are never complete, and people may want to change or add to theirs in the light of future thoughts and events. Some people will want to keep their story private; others might be happy to share it with a partner, family member, friend, support worker or professional. The PTMF website has a section ('Narrative

Construction') where we welcome wider sharing of PTMF-based narratives, anonymously if you wish. You can do this at **www.bps. org.uk/power-threat-meaning-framework/resources-training**

Chapter 10
How did we get here? Questioning some basic assumptions

We have deliberately left this chapter until near the end, because it contains some of the most challenging ideas in the whole book. It tackles the question of how we, as a whole society and culture, have come to accept a model of distress that is unsupported by research, lacking in effective treatments and often damaging in practice. It unpicks the beliefs and assumptions that have led to this state of affairs, tracing them back to their roots. In the West, these ideas and assumptions are so taken for granted they are almost invisible – they just seem to be facts about the way things are. Many of our readers will have this cultural heritage or will be influenced by it through living in the West or in a Westernised country.

This chapter is an opportunity to think about this important topic in more depth, and to address questions about how these ideas became so influential in our thinking about distress and troubling behaviour. The previous chapters have set the scene for what we hope will be a challenging and stimulating discussion about some of our most fundamental beliefs about ourselves and our relationship to the world we live in.

Examining some assumptions about ourselves

We have seen that psychiatric diagnosis is not simply a way of labelling or describing troubling emotions and behaviour. It involves a whole way of thinking about them that has persisted in spite of the lack of supporting evidence. There are many reasons for this staying power (see Johnstone & Boyle, 2018a, pp.29–31), but an important one is that this perspective is also part of a wider, Western cultural system of beliefs about our 'selves', our bodies and how we relate to the world. This system of beliefs encourages us to see ourselves as separate from each other and from the social and natural world, and to see thoughts as separate from emotions and physical reactions. It includes the idea that scientific theory and practice are not influenced by values and power. And it also informs the kinds of theories scientists develop about us and how they go about researching and gathering evidence. If we are to find lasting and more constructive ways forward, all of this needs to be open to question.

A good starting point is to acknowledge that what we might take for granted about our minds, emotions and behaviour is far from universal. How Western people think about these matters has been greatly influenced by a philosophical movement of the 17th and 18th centuries (and beyond) known as the European Enlightenment. Its leading figures[1] drew on and developed much older beliefs that the world consisted of stable, fixed laws that governed the movement of planets, the regularity of tides, the growth of crops, how much force could be applied to an object before it collapsed, what happened when two substances were mixed together, and so on. The Enlightenment scientists and philosophers believed that they could investigate these laws using reason and value-free inquiry as the source of accurate knowledge, rather than relying on the authority of the Church or state. As a consequence, intellect and reason were highly valued as guides, and contrasted with lesser-valued emotions and intuitions. However, not everyone was seen as having the same 'amount' of reason. White European men had most. Women, children, people not of European ancestry and those said to be 'mad' had far less. As we will see, these ideas still influence the relative importance given to different accounts of madness and mental distress.

Initially, Enlightenment ideas influenced the physical and natural sciences, such as astronomy, physics, chemistry and biology, and major advances were made in these fields. In the mid-19th century, Auguste Comte, a French philosopher, argued that

---

1. The leaders of the European enlightenment movement included René Descartes, Francis Bacon, David Hume, Immanuel Kant, John Locke and François-Marie Voltaire.

these ways of investigating the world, with careful measurement, experiments and so on, should also be used in the study of human affairs. He coined the term 'positivism' for this way of thinking. The new fields of sociology, psychology and psychiatry were enthusiastic supporters of Comte's ideas, partly because they hoped to achieve the same advances as the natural sciences and medicine, but also because imitating them offered credibility and status.

It is difficult to exaggerate the influence of all of this on Western worldviews. People raised in this cultural tradition may never have questioned the idea that reason is separate from emotion or that humans exist as separate individual selves, disconnected from each other and from the social and natural world. It can seem natural to talk about humans as if they are a type of machine – for example, the brain as a computer; being under pressure; feelings overflowing; needing to switch off. In this model, people are seen as objects that are acted on by external forces, and liable to biological and psychological malfunctions or breakdowns that need technological fixes. It also seems natural to talk about some thoughts or feelings as 'irrational' and to try to use the power of reason to change them. The idea that our troubling feelings and behaviour can, like the movement of the tides and planets, be described in the same way even in very different times and cultures, is still highly influential. So too is the view that it is the job of science to discover these laws of nature through experiments and measurements, and to make predictions and explanations.

The Enlightenment worldview has certainly had advantages. It has brought about huge advances in technology, medicine and many other areas. For example, it has given us heart surgery for blocked arteries and vaccinations to protect against disease. But applied wholesale by psychology and psychiatry, the positivist approach to understanding our thoughts, feelings and actions has serious limitations (see Johnstone & Boyle, 2018a, Chapter 2). One of these is downplaying spiritual beliefs and our relationship to the natural world, as we saw in Chapter 6 on 'Meaning' and Chapter 8 on 'General patterns in distress'. In this chapter, we'll discuss some of the other limitations including:

- seeing individuals as separate from each other and the social world

- the idea of various forms of distress as 'real', objective entities
- the way we understand the role of biology
- how researchers have gone about studying emotional and behavioural difficulties
- belief in the separation of facts from values
- how Westerners have viewed mental distress across cultures.

Separating us from each other and the social world

In Western societies, people often explain behaviour in terms of individual characteristics: I couldn't keep my New Year resolutions because I didn't have enough willpower; she did well in that job interview because she's so self-confident; he's had a bad time, but he'll be okay because he's very resilient. This is partly due to the influence of Enlightenment philosophy, with its emphasis on individual independence and autonomy. It also fits a culture that values personal achievement and material success. For example, 'getting on in life' might be explained by inborn abilities, high aspirations or ambition (and not getting on by the lack of them), rather than, say, by the availability of well-paid jobs, inherited wealth or social connections.

Psychologists and psychiatrists are part of this culture, so it is not surprising that their theories often reflect as well as reinforce it. Psychologists try to measure what are said to be our inner qualities, such as intelligence, self-esteem, self-efficacy, internal locus of control, and a whole range of personality characteristics. Cognitive psychologists often study processes such as perception, reasoning and memory quite separately from the contexts in which they are used. Errors, biases or dysfunctions in these processes are then used to 'explain' distress and troubling behaviour, and some types of individual therapy then develop techniques to correct these errors and return people to 'normal' psychological functioning. A belief in these inner qualities and their power to change people's lives extends to social and educational policy. For example, unemployed people may be told to attend courses that will increase their self-esteem, with the aim of making them more employable (Friedli & Stearn, 2015), or schools may try to teach 'character' or 'resilience' to young people to increase social mobility (Patterson et al., 2014).

Of course, our bodies provide a physical boundary separating us from each other and the external world. But our sense of ourselves as psychologically separate individuals whose actions arise from our inner characteristics can be very misleading. For example, 'willpower' may actually reflect how much support someone has in changing their behaviour, whether they have enough positive things in their life to give up something harmful, whether they have the time or money to pursue a different, healthier lifestyle or whether the harmful behaviour is helping them cope. It is much easier to give up a habit like smoking if you have other ways of dealing with stress and to avoid junk food if you live near decent shops and can afford more nutritious options. In her book on living in poverty, Linda Tirado described the important part smoking played in her life:

> It's expensive. It's also the best option. You see I'm always, always exhausted. It's a stimulant. When I'm too tired to walk one more step I can smoke and go for another hour. When I'm tired and beaten down and incapable of accomplishing one more thing, I can smoke and I feel a little better, just for a minute. (Tirado, 2014, p.xvii)

'Resilience' might be a result of knowing that someone is looking out for you or that you have the resources to change or leave a difficult situation. 'Self-confidence', or 'self-esteem' might be due to a history of positive experiences, perhaps helped by advantages such as wealth, attractiveness or sporting talent.[2]

We can go further and say that even what seem like our most individual, private experiences of thinking or making sense of what happens to us are also inseparable from our culture and our relationships. We are fundamentally social beings whose minds and brains develop in interaction with others, starting with our parents and carers, and our peer groups and wider society. The

---

2. The Midlands Psychology Group describe all of this in terms of 'embodied advantages someone has acquired over time from the social and material environment' – a more cumbersome phrase than will-power, self-confidence or resilience, but more credible than suggesting what they call 'essentially mysterious and unanalysable personal qualities that originate from within' (Midlands Psychology Group, 2013, p.124; see also their manifesto at www.midpsy.org/draft_manifesto.htm)

psychologist John Shotter (1993) and others (for example, Billig, 1996) have emphasised that how individuals think and feel about events and situations, however personal this seems, will always reflect how these situations are talked about and debated in the wider social world. We saw examples of this in Chapter 6, in the discussion about meaning. We may sometimes be physically alone with our thoughts, but we are rarely if ever socially or culturally alone with them.

It is not easy to do justice to all this using frameworks borrowed from medicine and the physical and biological sciences. As we noted in Chapter 2, our body parts and other physical objects don't have a social and cultural life; they don't reminisce with others about the past or plan the future. They don't create stories or social groups; they don't feel love, hate, loneliness or despair. They don't try to make sense of their experiences. These are characteristics of us as *persons.* They are all dependent on our social contexts and relationships and are vital in understanding our distress and troubling behaviour.

In the next section we look at another kind of separation that has resulted from the Enlightenment and the positivist worldview.

Mental disorders as separate 'things'

When we read or talk about 'mental health problems', we can easily forget that we are actually talking about what we are thinking, feeling and doing in relation to important aspects of our lives. Many diagnostic criteria are in fact descriptions of how we relate to others or how we feel in particular situations. Some diagnoses make no sense at all outside certain settings – could you have a 'personality disorder' or 'oppositional defiant disorder' or 'social anxiety disorder' if you were alone on a desert island? Yet, when a diagnosis is made, ways of feeling and behaving that may make perfect sense in context are transformed into a separate 'mental disorder' that someone 'has'. These 'disorders' seem to have a life of their own. They exist 'out there', as part of nature; they 'happen' to us; they 'develop' inside us; we are 'affected' by them; they cause us to think, feel and behave in certain ways; they can be targeted by certain drugs such as 'antidepressants' or 'antipsychotics'; they can be counted, studied and even treated without reference to our relationships or life circumstances. The language portrays us as containers acted on by outside forces, rather than human beings responding actively and meaningfully to our difficult lives. As mental health professionals David Jacobs and David Cohen put it (2010, p.312), when we are diagnosed with a mental disorder, we seem to have become,

> … through no intention or action of [our] own… the setting for the operation of impersonal, harmful cause–effect processes.

In fact, it is easy to find research papers on 'mental disorders' that hardly mention people at all. And, as we saw from David Kupfer's quote in Chapter 2, there is even the hope that these 'disorders' or 'impersonal, cause–effect processes' will one day be diagnosed 'using biological and genetic markers' – in other words, completely independent of people's actual lives and circumstances.

Jacqui Dillon, a psychiatric survivor and activist, has highlighted the muddled thinking arising from a belief in freestanding 'mental disorders'. She reports that, when people hear about her experience of horrific child sexual abuse, they often comment on how unlucky she was to 'get schizophrenia' as well (Dillon, 2016). This is just one example of a more general problem in thinking about 'mental disorders' as separate 'things' – it makes it harder to see the links between threats and threat responses (see Chapter 7).

It is a short jump from this to the idea that 'mental disorders' are fundamentally the same the world over, like broken legs, cancerous tumours, blocked arteries, bacterial infections and so on. We will return to this point later. Another consequence is the attempt to make historical diagnoses, as though 'disorders' are the same across time – Joan of Arc was really suffering from 'schizophrenia'; First World War soldiers were really suffering from 'post-traumatic stress disorder'; hysterical Victorian women were really suffering from 'major depressive disorder', and so on. It is not easy for Westerners to imagine a world without 'mental disorders'. A major aim of the PTMF is to show that the more we understand connections between what happens to people in their lives and the ways they respond, then the less we need to invent 'mental disorders' as an explanation.

The role of biology

In his book *Lost Connections*, journalist Johann Hari describes how hard it was for him to let go of the story he had been repeatedly told about his feelings of anxiety and depression – that they were caused by a problem in his brain, probably a chemical imbalance, and that they could be fixed by drugs. He also describes his surprise at finding how little evidence there is for this explanation (Hari, 2018).

As we've seen, versions of this story are repeated across the daily news, films, books, mental health websites and so on. It is a simple and hopeful story. It can also offer an alternative to a 'blame' narrative. It fits perfectly with the idea of 'mental disorders' as separate 'things' and with the seemingly endless search for biomarkers. It also fits with the Western practice of presenting biology as a cause of our thoughts, feelings and behaviour whose influence is not just separate from psychological processes or social contexts but more fundamental and important. Many psychology undergraduates have been taught courses called 'The Biological *Basis* of Behaviour' (emphasis added).[3] This creates a kind of hierarchy of human functioning, with biology providing the solid, essential foundation; psychology next, and culture/society perched on top. It can sometimes seem that, if we can find out 'what's going on' in the brain, then we don't need any other explanation for our behaviour.

This way of thinking often goes further, so that it's not unusual to find the brain described as if it has human characteristics. The increasingly popular area of neuroscience often conveys this, as in the title of a recent book, *The Secret Life of the Mind: How our brain thinks, feels and decides* (Sigman, 2019). But our brains do none of these things, no more than our muscles run marathons or our ears listen to music. *We*, as conscious persons, do these things. Brains and other bodily capacities *enable* us to run marathons and to appreciate music, of course. But we also participate in these things meaningfully, in relation to other people, to our life histories, our

---

3. In line with the idea of biology as the 'basis' of 'abnormal' behaviour, John Read and colleagues (2009) found that there were more than 20 times as many research papers published looking for biological causes of 'schizophrenia' or 'psychosis', than there were papers on social causes.

goals, social conventions and our material resources. And we do all this in ways that cannot be reduced to descriptions of how our brains function.

This doesn't mean we have an 'I' separate from our brains, floating inside our heads. It also doesn't mean ignoring biology in trying to understand how we think, feel or behave, or in how we become distressed. Far from it. But it does mean looking at the role of brains and biology in a different way.

In Chapter 7, on threat responses, we discussed some of the ways human beings can draw on various evolved, biologically based reactions that help us meet our needs and aid survival in the face of trauma and adversities. These are some general points about the role of biology and our bodies in distress:

▫   There are many theories about how our consciousness and the psychological and social processes that go with it, can arise from our physical brains. But this is still quite mysterious. However, it is clear that we are unlikely to be able to understand the meaningful behaviour of individuals by looking inside their brains. In other words:

> … no amount of neural knowledge would suffice to discriminate between writing one's name, copying one's name, practising one's signature, forging a name, writing an autograph, signing a cheque, witnessing a will, signing a death warrant, and so on. (Bennet & Hacker, 2003)

The key point is that our meaningful behaviour has to be understood in different terms from the biological processes that are part of it.

▫   However, it is also true that we can only experience the world and act on it through our bodies – this is partly what is meant by the term 'embodiment'. Our bodily abilities, expressed through our brains, sensory organs, limbs and so on, enable us to learn about and respond to the outside world, including, of course, other humans. They also put limits on what we can learn and do. The bodily feedback we call feelings is a fundamental part of this process. For example, life memories, pleasant and unpleasant, don't just include images, sounds, tastes or smells; they also include what we *felt*. How this bodily feedback is labelled, expressed and, very likely, experienced, varies across time and cultures and this partly accounts for variations in cultural expressions of distress.

□   As we saw in the discussion of threat responses, there are aspects of bodily responses that are particularly relevant in many experiences of distress, such as the capacity to fight, flee or freeze in response to threat; to become very alert or hypervigilant; to cut off from our awareness, or dissociate in the face of overwhelming events, and so on.

□   Our brains and biology, including our genetic make-up, are constantly shaped by our life experience. Indeed, a primary role of the brain is to change with experience, otherwise it would be difficult to learn or remember anything. We can therefore expect to find differences between the brains of people who have or haven't been given a psychiatric diagnosis, but this doesn't indicate that they are 'suffering from a brain disorder'. In fact, all our experiences will leave a trace on our brains and bodies, and in this way they will come to reflect not just the individual lives we have led but the kind of society we live in (Fine, 2012; Johnstone & Boyle, 2018a, pp.169–180; Rippon, 2020).

□   All of this produces complicated relationships and causal links between the social and material world and our brains, biology, feelings and behaviour. This contrasts with the simple links often implied by the illness model, where 'abnormal' biology is seen as a primary or basic cause. We still have much to learn about the nature of these links. But we do know that it makes no sense to try to extract a 'biologically based mental disorder' from our complex interpersonal, social, and economic networks (see also Johnstone & Boyle, 2018a, Chapter 5).

What do we know about 'mental disorders'?

Most of what counts as knowledge about mental health problems – the contents of textbooks, journal articles, the 'expert' views reported in the media – has been researched and written by people who may have experienced mental distress, as virtually all of us have, but who have not been given psychiatric diagnoses. This means that people's experience of extreme emotions, self-harm, compulsive rituals, dissociation, hearing voices and so on has largely been interpreted and explained by others. As the writer and psychiatric survivor Peter Beresford says, it is as if 'the greater the distance there is between direct experience and its interpretation, the more reliable the resulting knowledge' (Beresford, 2016, p.29). In other words, the message in our society is that the less personal experience you have of mental and emotional problems, the more suited you are to develop valid and influential knowledge about them (Russo & Sweeney, 2016).[4]

This state of affairs reflects several of the themes we've been discussing. First, there is the Enlightenment philosophers' view that some groups are less able to use reason and objectivity to find out about the world. Women, children and people of non-European ancestry were said to have less reason than white men, but people said to be mad had least of all. They were – still are – popularly said to have 'lost their reason', to be 'out of touch with reality' or to 'lack insight' into their 'illness'. Second, it is easier to dismiss personal knowledge if we believe that so-called mental disorders exist separately from the person, so that experts can study them objectively. Finally, by using methods borrowed from physical and biological science, psychology and psychiatry have given higher status to experiments, measurement, statistical techniques and so on, as ways of discovering 'facts' about our thinking, feeling and behaviour, and given less status and attention to subjective experience and personal meaning.

It is difficult to exaggerate the lasting influence of beliefs about the unequal distribution of reason. The views of women and other subordinate groups were already marginalised. But the Enlightenment philosophy entrenched these beliefs in the

---

4. In earlier times, and even into the 20th century, people in psychiatric facilities were not just excluded from the creation of 'scientific' knowledge but discouraged from or forbidden to record their experiences. They were deprived of writing materials or writing was viewed with suspicion by staff. Some went to great lengths to record their feelings and experiences indirectly (see, for example, Gail Hornstein's book (2012) *Agnes's Jacket*. The title of this book refers to Agnes Richter, a skilled seamstress committed to a 19th century German asylum. Probably deprived of writing materials, she stitched what seem like fragments of her thoughts and feelings (they are not easy to decipher) on the inside of her jacket. Even today, it can still feel risky to speak frankly, especially if you are held under section.

new scientific age, making it even more difficult for marginalised groups to create influential knowledge, even about themselves. Instead, the new 'science' produced many theories justifying why they were not suited to doing this. This was often because they were held to be closer to emotion, bodies, and nature. Thus, their main role was to be *objects* of study by others.

The emphasis on reason also relates to the belief that we can and should separate 'facts' from 'values' in gaining knowledge about ourselves and the world. Scientists from this tradition often portray themselves as neutral observers whose training and methods allow them to discover objective 'facts', uninfluenced by personal interests or prejudices. Measurements and statistics have certainly been useful in looking at some aspects of our personal lives. We might measure the effect of different amounts of alcohol on drivers' reaction times or investigate links between income and prescriptions for psychiatric drugs. But in the case of our relationships and social world, this approach also misses a great deal, not least because of the huge importance of *meaning*. For example, a Life Stress Scale might rate getting divorced as much more stressful than starting a new job, which could be true for some people but reversed for others.

Researchers typically decide in advance what should be measured, what questions people should be asked and what form of answers are acceptable. They then have to decide what these answers, or the numbers that represent them, actually mean. But this runs the risk of introducing personal bias and cultural influences, and, as a result, important questions can remain unasked and important knowledge unrecorded. And what remains unrecorded has often been aspects of people's lives where the abuse of power is central. For example, until recently, life experiences that are strongly linked to mental health problems, such as child sexual abuse, poverty, domestic violence and racial and other kinds of discrimination, were hardly mentioned in mainstream theories or interventions.[5]

Fortunately, this is changing. People with first-hand experience of extreme emotions, unusual psychological states and troubling

---

5. For critical exploration of how lack of attention to 'race', ethnicity and gender has biased research in the mental health field, we recommend Fernando (2010), Stoppard (2000) and Ussher (2011).

behaviour ('experts by experience') are much more involved in creating influential knowledge (see, for example, Cameron et al., 2018; Russo & Sweeney, 2016; Wallcraft et al., 2009). So too are other groups marginalised by Enlightenment philosophy, such as women and people not of European ancestry. Qualitative research, which engages more directly with people's experiences and doesn't convert them into numbers, is more widely used (Harper & Thompson, 2012). But progress is slow and unsteady. This kind of knowledge is still far from mainstream. There is also still a hierarchy of evidence used in evaluating drugs and therapies for mental health problems, as well as in judging the quality of research itself more generally. Here, findings based on numbers, measurements and statistics are given higher status, while first-person accounts can still be downgraded to 'anecdote' or 'opinion'. Thus, definitions of what counts as official 'knowledge' or 'facts' can be used to protect those with vested interests and silence those with less power. For example, pharmaceutical companies have continued to profit from increased drug prescriptions while people's personal reports of withdrawal effects from tranquillisers and antidepressants have been dismissed for years.[6]

As we've seen, the PTMF includes but goes beyond traditional sources of evidence and knowledge creation to enable us to highlight the importance of power and meaning. Indeed, it is only by adopting this wider perspective that we were able to develop the framework at all.

Cross-cultural perspectives

Western views on distress are increasingly being applied or imposed around the world, supported by the Movement for Global Mental Health (Wainberg et al., 2017).[7] Its aim is to 'scale up' psychiatric services in low-income and middle-income countries where there is said to be a 'treatment gap', depriving the majority

---

6. Service user testimony is not directly mentioned in the National Institute for Health and Care Excellence (NICE) 'hierarchy of statistical information' used to assess the effectiveness of medical and social care interventions, although it may be included indirectly, interpreted by others, in some types of so-called weaker evidence, such as case studies or 'clinical experience of respected authorities' (see also Davies & Read, 2019; Read et al, 2018).

7. See www.mhinnovation.net/organisations/movement-global-mental-health-mgmh

of people of Western interventions. This is another example of the Enlightenment assumptions that Western knowledge is more objective and rational, Western medicine is better equipped to treat the disorders its diagnostic processes identify, and that 'mental disorders' are biologically based and fundamentally the same all around the world.

The Movement for Global Mental Health has been strongly criticised for its 'medical imperialism' in imposing particular ways of thinking on very different cultures. This has been described as a new form of colonialism, less obvious but just as damaging as earlier versions (Mills & Fernando, 2014). In fact, many non-Western cultures are based on very different assumptions from those of Enlightenment philosophy. For example, in Chapter 6 on 'Meaning', we noted that the Iban people of Malaysia do not distinguish between thinking, in the internal Western sense, and talking, and that the Iban notion of thinking is intimately tied up with emotion, desire and will. This is very different from the Western separation of thinking and feeling. As well as these more abstract aspects, it has been known for some time that outcomes, even from the extremes of distress diagnosed as 'schizophrenia', are more favourable in non-Western countries. One of many factors may be lower use of 'antipsychotic' drugs (Davidson & McGlashan, 1997; Warner, 2004). In other words, in the field of distress, Westerners may have more to learn and less to offer than is often assumed.

The sections in *DSM-IV* on 'culture-bound syndromes' and in *DSM-5* on 'cultural concepts of distress' tell us a lot about the struggle to incorporate Western diagnostic approaches into the many ways distress is experienced and expressed across cultures. As we saw in Chapter 7 on threat responses, the list of 'culture-bound syndromes' in *DSM-IV* failed to acknowledge that Western expressions of distress are just as culture bound as any other. In the face of criticism, *DSM-5* replaced 'culture-bound syndromes' with a more elaborate discussion of 'cultural concepts of distress'. However, this still retains the fundamental assumptions of Western scientific superiority and the existence of separate, diagnosable mental disorders. For example, cultural concepts of distress are said to be important to avoid misdiagnosis and improve engagement with clinicians and treatment outcomes.

They are also said to be important in helping to 'identify patterns of comorbidity', or medical conditions that occur together, and in finding underlying biological factors (APA, 2013, pp.758–759; see also the main PTMF document, pages 67–72 and Chapter 6, and Chapter 8 of this book). In other words, 'cultural concepts' are mainly being used to support Western-style diagnosis, treatment and research.

We have shown that the PTMF takes a very different view of cultural diversity of experiences and expressions of distress. As we emphasised in Chapter 2, almost all psychiatric diagnoses are based on cultural norms. There is no evidence for any underlying, universal, biological 'disorder' that means we can decide what illness the person is 'really' suffering from, and there is never likely to be. If we see distress and troubling behaviours not as symptoms of underlying illness but as socially meaningful responses to adversity, then our responses will inevitably vary across cultures. But there will also be cross-cultural similarities, because we all share fundamental human characteristics, such as seeking close relationships and being saddened by loss, angered by insults and fearful of physical harm, or becoming so overwhelmed by feelings that our perceptions of the world get distorted. The PTMF can accommodate – and expects – these similarities and differences.

However, as we also emphasised in Chapter 8, the PTMF is not intended for export in the same way as the Movement for Global Mental Health. It was developed in a Western context and inevitably reflects the personal, group and community dilemmas posed by Western culture. But the framework also includes factors not often found in Western psychiatric and psychological models, such as the impact of colonialism, war, transgenerational trauma and loss of identity culture, language, heritage and land. As we've said, our hope is that the PTMF can stand alongside culturally very diverse and different approaches in such a way that each can respect, support and learn from the other.

What are the implications for alternatives to diagnosis?

The underlying assumptions we've discussed are still very powerful in shaping how we think about our emotional distress and troubled or troubling behaviour, and in supporting belief in the diagnostic approach. However the influence of these assumptions goes well beyond that, and they serve many political, economic and social interests. For example, as we discussed in Chapter 4, the economic philosophy called neoliberalism, now very influential in many Western countries, relies on the idea of independent, rational individuals competing with each other to achieve and consume. More generally, the diagnostic perspective, in locating the causes of distress within individuals rather than in social structures, has been a highly effective way of concealing and perpetuating the negative operation of power and silencing dissenting voices. This function is all the more important at times of social and economic upheaval that require effective control systems to deal with the human consequences.

Many critics have argued that this double function – where 'psychiatry is required to be the agent of society while purporting to be agent of the individual' (Johnstone, 2000, p.218) – is vital in explaining why the diagnostic model is so persistent in spite of lack of evidence in its support and much evidence of the harm it can do. The scientific rhetoric that surrounds diagnosis is also a key part of this. It is perhaps not surprising that, as industrialised societies face deepening crises – conflict, fragmented families and communities, economic inequality, loss of traditional roles and rituals, destruction of the natural environment and so on – diagnostic thinking is so popular. [8]

At the same time, the innocuous-sounding term 'mental health', which of course implies the existence of 'mental illness', is also increasingly popular (Johnstone, 2020a). We are encouraged to see 'mental health' as something we all 'have' and need to 'look after', including by diagnosing ourselves through self-help books or websites, or by seeking professional help.

Looked at in PTMF terms, we are seeing a massive rise in material, social and relational threats, and a resulting increase in threat responses, along with strong social pressure to disconnect the two and to label oneself as having 'mental health problems' instead. But we are also seeing signs of resistance to the diagnostic perspective. For example, although COVID-19 triggered numerous

---

8. Nor is it a new phenomenon: medical and diagnostic perspectives on 'insanity' became dominant in the 19th-century during a time of rapid industrialisation, when there were large increases in numbers of people confined in asylums.

predictions of an 'epidemic of mental disorders' (Harvey, 2020; Daley, 2020), it also inspired articles pointing out the completely understandable reasons for feeling anxious and miserable, and the need to find solutions in building fairer societies, not simply prescribing more pills (Johnstone, 2020b; The Wisdom Collector, 2020). The enthusiastic response to the PTMF in many quarters suggests that many people are ready for a radical new perspective. We may be reaching a tipping point, and each individual who chooses to question and re-write their own diagnostic story, or to support others to do so, is a part of the much-needed change.

It will not be easy to move away from the assumptions that have shaped and support what we've called the 'DSM mindset'. We hope we have shown that adopting a different perspective offers the possibility of a more constructive, hopeful, non-pathologising and evidence-based understanding of emotional distress and troubled and troubling behaviour. This different perspective allows us to see much more clearly the links between distress, social inequalities and social injustice. In the final chapter, we briefly discuss some of the wider implications of moving away from a diagnostic approach, and point readers towards useful reading and resources.

Chapter 11
Further implications of the Power Threat Meaning Framework

This book has focused mainly on the PTMF as a way of understanding the distress we all experience at times, and how its principles can be used to develop personal narratives as an alternative to psychiatric diagnosis. However, the diagnostic perspective is very deeply embedded in many other systems and institutions, and if we are to move beyond this particular model once and for all, we need to suggest alternatives in these areas as well.

Chapter 8 of the main PTMF document (Johnstone & Boyle, 2018) makes suggestions for how we might replace diagnostic terms and assumptions in the areas of public health policy; mental health policy; service principles; service design, commissioning and outcomes; access to social care, housing and welfare benefits; therapeutic interventions; the legal system, and research. It shows that, in many cases, alternatives already exist. For example, a number of services base their entry criteria on general terms such as 'severe and persistent' or 'complex and enduring' difficulties, rather than on diagnostic categories. Readers can look at Chapter 8 itself for more details, but some of the areas that often raise questions are discussed below.

Access to social care, housing and welfare benefits

The PTMF states at several points that the overriding priority is to protect service-user rights to essential resources and support. 'In the short and medium term, psychiatric diagnoses will still be required for people to access services, benefits and so on. These rights must be protected' (Johnstone & Boyle, 2018a, p.18). At the same time, it argues that the current system is not working. Benefits are grossly inadequate, the application process is confusing and stressful, and having a diagnosis is no guarantee of success. Moreover, while some people are happy to have a diagnosis, others resent the necessity of taking on a stigmatising label in order to be awarded the bare minimum to survive.

The PTMF therefore aims to open up a much-needed discussion about hypothetical alternatives, all of which have their pros and cons. A personal narrative is obviously not suitable for these purposes, but another possibility is using straightforward problem descriptions such as 'hearing distressing voices' or 'feeling suicidal' or 'experiencing severe anxiety'. A GP signing you off work might say you have 'stress' or 'exhaustion'; in the same way, these are non-medical terms that do not need to include personal details but are acceptable if confirmed by a professional. More radical solutions such as Universal Basic Income, in which everyone is guaranteed a basic living wage regardless of their employment or health status, are also worth considering, although a lot depends on how they are implemented. A universal right to income has been found to be popular with service users as an alternative to the humiliating requirement to demonstrate enough impairment to access essential financial support (Beresford et al., 2016).

Use of psychiatric drugs

As we discussed in Chapter 2, the PTMF recognises that some people find psychiatric drugs helpful. However, it argues that it is rare for people to be fully informed about their possible limitations and drawbacks, with the result that they are routinely misused and over-used. Psychiatrist Joanna Moncrieff has described the difference between the 'disease-centred' and the 'drug-centred' models of drug action (Moncrieff, 2013; 2020). The former describes the situation when medications directly affect the biological causes of disease and bodily symptoms (e.g. replacing the body's insulin supply, destroying cancerous tumours, killing bacteria and so on). The latter argues that, rather like street drugs or alcohol, psychiatric drugs have a range of general effects, such as sedation or emotional blunting, on both 'normal' and 'abnormal' states of mind. This may be helpful in extreme or overwhelming distress, and no one would want to deny people that kind of relief. Equally, it may be unhelpful in everyday life, as service users often report. However, it is not accurate to describe this as 'treatment' for a 'medical illness' any more than we would describe a glass of wine as 'treatment' for 'social anxiety'. Neither the PTMF nor the drug-centred model of action justify telling people that psychiatric drugs are essential to their recovery or must be taken long-term (although people may choose to do this), and nor are there grounds for administering them against people's will. The PTMF argues that support to come off psychiatric drugs needs to be routinely available.

(Please note that it is dangerous to reduce or stop your drugs without taking professional advice. Useful resources can be found at the end of this chapter.)

Research

Diagnostic categories are often said to be essential for research. This has become a vicious circle. Some researchers openly acknowledge the limitations of these terms but continue to use them because journals require them. Regulatory bodies such as the National Institute for Health and Care Excellence (NICE) then base their guidelines on these 'conditions' and, as a consequence, research funders award grants for further investigations into them. The irony is that studies based on non-valid categories are unlikely to come up with anything useful. For this reason, the world's largest funding body for mental health research, the National Institute for Mental Health (NIMH) in the US, has taken the highly significant step of 're-orienting its research away from *DSM* categories' (Insel, 2013).[1]

Chapter 8 of the main PTMF document (Johnstone & Boyle, 2018) summarises a wide range of alternative strategies that do not have to be based on diagnostic categories. For example, use of the ordinary descriptive term 'hearing voices' has been very productive in the large body of research emerging out of the

---

1. However, it should be noted that Thomas Insel, a former NIMH director, and other critical psychiatrists, such as Dr Allen Frances, who chaired the committee that produced *DSM-IV*, are not abandoning the idea of psychiatric diagnosis as such. They continue to hope that research into new systems will one day put it on a firmer footing.

Hearing Voices movement (Longden, 2017). Traditional research methodologies have uses for certain purposes, as we said in the previous chapter, but we also need to place equal value on the kinds of evidence that are overlooked or discounted within what counts as 'evidence-based practice', such as people's personal accounts of their experiences. Survivor researchers have called for the opportunity to develop their own non-diagnostic research frameworks that will allow their voices and experiences to be valued and heard (Sweeney, 2016).

Social and public health policy

By this stage in the book, it will be obvious that the PTMF has important implications for social policy and public health. Chapter 8 of the main PTMF document summarises these as:

- reducing economic and social inequality, which is probably the single most effective step we can take to improve the emotional wellbeing of the population, especially in groups who have less power because of class, age, ethnicity, sexuality and/or gender

- recognising the profound psychological, educational, occupational, social, and economic impact and cost of adversities of all kinds, especially if they occur early in life

- offering support for families and early-years child development

- recognising that the negative effects of psychiatric drugs are a major public health concern

- and finally, since war is the biggest cause of distress worldwide, conflict resolution should be an international priority.

Much of this is already recognised, if not acted on, but the PTMF argues that all these priorities will be undermined by continuing to frame emotional and psychological distress in diagnostic terms, thereby disconnecting the threat responses from the threats. We must not lose sight of the fact that, as a World Health Organization Commission on Social Determinants of Health (2008) concluded, 'Social injustice is killing people on a grand scale'.

Language

In Chapter 4, we discussed the ways in which power operates through words and language. This is why we see language use as one of the most important areas of change, underpinning all the others. It needs to go much further than exchanging one word (such as 'schizophrenia') for another (such as 'psychosis'). Rather, we need to have a whole new discourse about the experiences grouped under the term 'mental health'. (At the start of this book we explained why we have used this term at times – although it is unsatisfactory because it also implies its opposite, 'illness'.) The automatic use of words like 'symptom', 'patient', 'treatment', 'prognosis', 'medications', 'pathology', 'disorder' and so on to describe emotional suffering shapes the whole way we think about these experiences, so that it seems bizarre to question the familiar landscape of hospitals and clinics staffed by doctors and nurses relying heavily on diagnoses and drugs. As we say in Chapter 8 of the PTMF *Overview*:

> … changing language is not simply about using alternative vocabulary, but opens up new ways of thinking, experiencing and acting. Until this happens, we will simply continue to reproduce existing practices in slightly different, but equally unsatisfactory, forms. (Johnstone & Boyle, 2018b, p.313).

We, the authors, like some readers no doubt, have lived through numerous changes of service design and delivery, seen new teams proliferate and new drugs and therapies marketed, while new theories and therapies come and go. The so-called 'mental health epidemic' has increased in parallel, as each thinly disguised version of the same old medical language and assumptions fails to provide the hoped-for path to recovery. This cycle is doomed to continue until we are able to leave behind the current diagnostic language and assumptions – the whole 'DSM mindset', as we have called it.

People in distress have a right to describe their difficulties as they wish and, as we noted at the start of the book, may need to use diagnostic terms for practical reasons such as access to resources or to find relevant literature and self-help groups, whether they agree with them or not. Some people will continue to find diagnostic terms a useful shorthand description of their problems. Others find that the diagnostic model makes sense to them. However, the right to choice of language typically works in one direction only. Those who want their difficulties defined in diagnostic terms are unlikely to be denied this. The corresponding right, to refuse psychiatric labels or to be informed about debates around and the limitations of this model, is rarely if ever offered and may be actively resisted. As one person said:

> Service users who identify with their diagnosis – you have pretty much an *entire* mental health system that agrees and supports your perspective. Those of us who feel utterly hopeless and oppressed by our diagnosis – where do we go? (Quoted in Johnstone et al., 2019, p.48)

We argue that professionals, researchers, lecturers, charities, policy-makers and journalists should be using language that reflects an accurate and evidence-based view of the problems they are describing. The diagnostic discourse does not do this. For this reason, the position of the PTMF is that 'it can no longer be considered professionally, scientifically or ethically justifiable to present psychiatric diagnoses as if they were valid statements about people and their difficulties' (Johnstone & Boyle, 2018a, p. 316).

It is not always easy to find acceptable alternative terms. Sometimes an everyday word or descriptive phrase will do instead. For example, we can replace 'symptom' with 'problem' or 'difficulty'; for 'schizophrenia', 'bipolar disorder' or 'depressive illness' we can substitute 'hearing voices', 'having extreme mood swings', or 'feeling desperate and suicidal'. We can turn the conditions that people are said to 'have' into what they 'do': for example, 'experiencing the effects of trauma' rather than 'having a personality disorder'. Sometimes we may need a range of alternatives to draw on: for example, replacing 'mental illness' with 'emotional distress', 'mental distress', 'severe mental distress', 'extreme state', 'psychological distress', 'troubled or troubling behaviour' and 'emotional suffering'.

The struggle to develop a satisfactory non-medical discourse, one that opens up rather than closes down new ways of understanding, is at the heart of the paradigm shift that is needed. As we've discussed extensively in this book, attention to language is essential if we are to challenge and change epistemic injustice and the ideological power that underpins dominant cultural narratives of distress.

Reactions to the PTMF

Since its launch in January 2018, the PTMF has had a bigger impact than we could ever have anticipated. At the time of writing, two years on, the project team has been invited to deliver more than 200 presentations and workshops across the UK and in Ireland, Denmark, Spain, Greece, Brazil, the US, Australia, New Zealand and South Korea. The main document and the overview of the PTMF have both been translated into Spanish, and translations into four other languages are in hand. The PTMF website gives examples of where the PTMF is informing clinical work in the fields of intellectual disability, older adults, children and adolescents, forensic and prison services and health, and its growing influence in other areas of policy, practice and research. It has also been welcomed by peer groups, as described in the previous chapter. Pilot studies and evaluations are starting to come in, and all of this will, in due course, feed back into revised versions of the PTMF.

Inevitably, since the PTMF poses a major challenge to the dominant diagnostic model, it has not been welcomed by everyone. The authors have written a joint response to some of the comments and criticisms on social media and elsewhere (Johnstone et al., 2019). We are very much open to further feedback as the PTMF develops.

PTMF resources and developments

We encourage interested readers to visit the PTMF website. It hosts an evolving set of resources, including FAQs, videos, training materials, articles, blogs, events, projects and evaluations.[2] There is also a contact form for comments, queries and feedback. Priorities for the next stage of the PTMF are:

- further development and evaluation of the general patterns
- producing accessible versions and materials suitable for particular groups (people with learning disabilities, children, the general public and so on)

---

2. www.bps.org.uk/power-threat-meaning-framework/resources-training

- building up a PTMF training community, in partnership with service users

- ensuring wide representation in further developments, especially of service users and people from different cultural and ethnic backgrounds

- evaluation of other aspects of the PTMF, using a range of methodologies

- linking with groups who may wish to develop the PTMF in line with their own cultural beliefs and contexts

- linking with journalists, policy makers, campaigners and other key players and organisations in the mental health field.

For people interested in exploring the arguments further and perhaps finding non-diagnostic services and organisations, further lists of publications, websites and other resources can be found at the end of the book, on pages 175–181.

Conclusion

A recent United Nations report aligns with the arguments of the PTMF:

> Many of the concepts supporting the biomedical model in mental health have failed to be confirmed by further research. Diagnostic tools, such as the *International Classification of Diseases* and the *Diagnostic and Statistical Manual of Mental Disorders*, continue to expand the parameters of individual diagnosis, often without a solid scientific basis... The urgent need for a shift in approach should prioritize policy innovation at the population level, targeting social determinants and abandon the predominant medical model that seeks to cure individuals by targeting 'disorders'... Mental health policies should address the 'power imbalance' rather than 'chemical imbalance'. (Office of the High Commissioner for Human Rights, 2017, p.19)

Most of us do not have the power or influence to bring about change at that level, but all of us can, with the right information, make our own choices about moving on from the diagnostic model of distress in the context of our own lives. In this way we may, as survivors Jacqui Dillon and Rufus May have put it, be able to create new narratives that 'transform discourses of deficit into ones of strength and survival' as part of 'our right to define ourselves; the right to find our own voices'. This includes seeing your experiences as valid and meaningful; putting them in a wider context of social justice; joining together with others; and sometimes finding a new purpose that emerges out of suffering' (Dillon & May, 2003p.16). We hope this introduction to the PTMF will be a contribution to that process.

Further reading and resources

Books

All the books in the 'Straight Talking Introduction' series, published by PCCS Books, are recommended. They include:

A Straight Talking Introduction to Being a Mental Health Service User, by Peter Beresford (2010)

A Straight Talking Introduction to Caring for Someone with Mental Health Problems, edited by Jen Kilyon and Theresa Smith (2009)

A Straight Talking Introduction to Children's Mental Health Problems, by Sami Timimi (2009). A highly recommended critique of current psychiatric practices that takes a non-diagnostic perspective.

A Straight Talking Introduction to Psychiatric Diagnosis, by Lucy Johnstone (2014). This is particularly relevant for those wishing to explore the debates about diagnosis further.

A Straight Talking Introduction to Psychiatric Drugs: The truth about how they work and how to come off them, by Joanna Moncrieff (2020). This updated and rewritten second edition scrutinises and critiques the evidence for the 'chemical imbalance' hypothesis on which psychiatric drug prescribing is based and the effects of these drugs. Highly recommended.

A Straight Talking Introduction to the Causes of Mental Health Problems, by John Read and Pete Sanders (2010). A clear explanation of all the factors that lead to diagnoses for 'mental health problems'.

We also recommend the following:

A Manifesto for Mental Health: Why we need a revolution in mental health care, by Peter Kinderman. Palgrave Macmillan (2019). A professor of psychology proposes a radical new way of organising and running our mental health system.

Anatomy of an Epidemic: Magic bullets, psychiatric drugs, and the astonishing rise of mental illness in America, by Robert Whitaker. Crown Publishing Group (2011). A compelling overview of the research on psychiatric drugs, arguing that overall they create more disability than they cure.

Beyond Belief: Alternative ways of working with delusions, obsessions and unusual experiences, by Tamasin Knight. Peter Lehmann Publishing (2013). Offers a new way of helping people deal with unusual beliefs by encouraging supporters to consider working within the person's belief system. Downloadable free from www.peter-lehmann-publishing.com/books/knight.htm

Cracked: Why psychiatry is doing more harm than good, by James Davies. Icon Books (2013). James Davies' extraordinary investigation into how the *DSM* is created, featuring interviews with the committee members.

Crazy Like Us: The globalisation of the Western mind, by Ethan Watters. Constable & Robinson (2011). A hard-hitting look at the damaging effects of exporting the Western diagnostic model across the world.

De-medicalising Misery: Psychiatry, psychology and the human condition, edited by Mark Rapley, Joanna Moncrieff and Jacqui Dillon. Palgrave Macmillan (2011). An inspiring collection of essays about non-medical approaches to distress.

Doctoring the Mind: Why psychiatric treatments fail, by Richard Bentall. Allen Lane/Penguin (2009). A thorough, research-based overview of the currently available psychiatric interventions and their limitations

Drop the Disorder! Challenging the culture of psychiatric diagnosis, edited by Jo Watson. PCCS Books (2019). Chapters by a wide range of contributors, both professionals and survivors, who are committed to offering alternatives to the diagnostic model of distress.

Experiencing Psychosis: Personal and professional perspectives, edited by Jim Geekie, Patte Randall, Debra Lampshire and John Read. Routledge (2011). Examines first-person accounts alongside current research to suggest how personal experience can contribute professionals' attempts to understand and help.

Formulation in Psychology and Psychotherapy: Making sense of people's problems (2nd ed.), edited by Lucy Johnstone and Rudi Dallos. Routledge (2013). A comprehensive overview of formulation-based practice.

Living with Voices: 50 stories of recovery, edited by Marius Romme, Sandra Escher, Jacqui Dillon, Dirk Corstens and Mervyn Morris. PCCS Books (2009). Fifty people describe how they have overcome their problems with hearing voices outside of the illness model, by overcoming feelings of threat and powerlessness and discovering that voices are not a sign of madness but a reaction to problems in their lives.

Lost Connections: Why you're depressed and how to find hope, by Johann Hari. Bloomsbury (2018). Journalist Johann Hari takes a fascinating journey through what we know about depression, based partly on his own experiences of diagnosis and psychiatric drugs.

Madness Contested: Power and practice, by Steven Coles, Sarah Keenan and Bob Diamond. PCCS Books (2013). A readable collection of essays looking at criticisms of and alternatives to current mental health practice.

Models of Madness: Psychological, social and biological approaches to psychosis, edited by John Read and Jacqui Dillon. Routledge (2013). A comprehensive overview of critiques of all aspects of psychiatric theory and practice

Our Encounters with Madness, edited by Alec Grant, Francis Biley and Hannah Walker. PCCS Books (2011). An edited collection of 36 service user and carer accounts of diagnosis, personal experience, and the psychiatric system. The stories are frank, varied and uncensored.

Searching for a Rose Garden: Challenging psychiatry, fostering mad studies, edited by Jasna Russo and Angela Sweeney. PCCS Books (2016). A collection of radical critiques of the psychiatric system, authored by survivors.

Sky-diving for Beginners: A journey of recovery and hope, by Jo MacFarlane. Scottish Independent Advocacy Alliance (2014). Jo MacFarlane takes us through her journey to recovery in this moving account. Available from edinburghjo@yahoo.co.uk

Tales from the Madhouse: An insider critique of psychiatric services, by Gary Sidley. PCCS Books (2015). Clinical psychologist Gary Sidley reflects on a career in mental health services and calls for change.

The Body Keeps the Score: Mind, brain and body in the transformation of trauma, by Bessel van der Kolk. Viking (2014). A thoughtful and inspiring overview of the trauma-informed approach by one of its leading proponents.

The Spirit Level: Why equality is better for everyone, by Richard Wilkinson and Kate Pickett. London: Allen Lane (2010). Influential and accessible analysis of the effects of economic inequality on all aspects of our lives, including emotional wellbeing.

This Book Will Change your Mind about Mental Health: A journey into the heartland of psychiatry, by Nathan Filer. Faber and Faber (2019). Former mental health nurse Nathan Filer examines the stories of people diagnosed with 'schizophrenia' in this accessible exploration of current debates in mental health.

Trauma and Recovery: From domestic abuse to political terror, by Judith Herman. Basic Books (2015). A classic, profound and moving account of the role of trauma in all our lives, from the personal to the political.

Understanding Mental Health and Distress: Beyond abnormal psychology, edited by John Cromby, David Harper and Paula Reavey. Palgrave Macmillan (2013). The first UK undergraduate textbook to be co-authored with service users and to be based on a non-diagnostic perspective.

Reports

The Division of Clinical Psychology within the British Psychological Society has published two accessible reports that argue that people have the right to choose their own understanding of their distress, which may or may not be a medical one, and their own preferred forms of help. The reports include comprehensive lists of resources. They are:

Understanding Diagnosis in Adult Mental Health. British Psychological Society (2016). This leaflet summarises some of the main debates about psychiatric diagnosis. Available at https://www.bps.org.uk/sites/www.bps.org.uk/files/Member%20Networks/Divisions/DCP/Understanding%20psychiatric%20diagnosis%20in%20adult%20mental%20health.pdf

Understanding Psychosis and Schizophrenia (revised ed.), edited by Anne Cooke. British Psychological Society (2017). An accessible publication that opens up new ways of understanding the experiences that are labelled as 'psychosis' and 'schizophrenia'. Available at www.understandingpsychosis.net

Blogs

Behaviourism and Mental Health. www.behaviorismandmentalhealth.com Psychologist Phil Hickey's powerful critiques of psychiatric theory and practice.

Laura Delano. www.lauradelano.com Laura Delano's website and blog tells the story of her recovery from 13 years in the psychiatric system.

Me, myself and disability. www.memyselfanddisability.wordpress.com Chris Coombs writes about his reflections on mental distress and physical disability.

Retired Discursive of Tunbridge Wells. https://blogs.canterbury.ac.uk/discursive Articles and interviews on a range of mental health topics.

Tales from the Madhouse. www.talesfromthemadhouse.com Clinical psychologist Gary Sidley blogs about an insider's critique of psychiatric services.

The Blog That Shouldn't Be Written: Madness, trauma and recovery. www.indigodaya.com Campaigner and a survivor of psychiatry, Indigo Daya tells her story in these blogs.

Websites

A Disorder for Everyone. www.adisorder4everyone.com A collection of talks, articles and resources supporting the 'A Disorder for Everyone' events, which challenge traditional psychiatric theory and practice.

A Disorder for Everyone on YouTube. www.youtube.com/channel/UCaWG15Tqjo6sZ7obcnKc_Mw Inspiring collection of talks and interviews with leading professionals, campaigners and activists.

Auntie Psychiatry. www.auntiepsychiatry.com/Auntie%20Psychiatry.html A collection of hard-hitting cartoons by the talented Auntie Psychiatry.

Coming Off. www.comingoff.com A website to support those wishing to withdraw from psychiatric drugs.

Dolly Sen. www.dollysen.com Dolly Sen is an award-winning writer, artist, performer and filmmaker and an activist for change in psychiatry.

Dr Terry Lynch. www.doctorterrylynch.com GP Dr Terry Lynch challenges the medical model of depression in his courses and resources.

Drop the Disorder Facebook group. www.facebook.com/groups/ 1182483948461309 A group for debate about alternatives to current psychiatric practice.

Emerging Proud. www.emergingproud.com Resources, support and personal stories for people who see their crises in spiritual, mystical or transcendent terms.

Hearing Voices Network. www.hearing-voices.org Offers information, support and understanding to people who hear voices and those who support them. It also aims to promote awareness, tolerance and understanding of voice hearing, visions, tactile sensations and other unusual experiences.

I Got Better. www.igotbetter.org A collection of videos by people who see themselves as having recovered.

Jacqui Dillon. www.jacquidillon.org Trainer, writer and voice-hearer Jacqui Dillon's website. She also describes her experiences of rejecting psychiatry at www.youtube.com/watch?v=JHzHliy5yeQ

Mad in America. www.madinamerica.com An invaluable resource for critical perspectives on all aspects of mental health. Includes inspiring blogs by a number of former service users who are now activists and campaigners

Mad in the UK. www.madintheUK.com One of Mad in America's sister sites, which hosts a UK-oriented collection of blogs, articles and resources.

Mind Freedom. www.mindfreedom.org/personal-stories Mind Freedom aims to 'win human rights campaigns in mental health, challenge abuse by the psychiatric drug industry, support the self-determination of psychiatric survivors and mental health consumers and promote safe, humane and effective options in mental health'. The website also has a large collection of personal stories.

National Paranoia Network. www.nationalparanoianetwork.org Website with ideas and resources for people experiencing suspicious thoughts and paranoia.

National Survivor User Network. www.nsun.org.uk The NSUN network for mental health is an independent, service-user-led charity that connects people with experience of mental health issues to give them a stronger voice in shaping policy and services. Includes information about service user groups, activities and resources across the country.

Paranoid Thoughts. www.paranoidthoughts.com Clinical psychologist and self-help book author, Daniel Freeman hosts this website about 'unfounded or excessive fears about others'. Includes first-person accounts by people who have experienced suspicious thoughts and paranoia.

Paula J. Caplan. www.paulajcaplan.net Articles, books and links by Paula Caplan, US psychologist and leading campaigner against psychiatric labels.

Rufus May. https://rufusmay.com Rufus May is a clinical psychologist and former service user who hosts a range of resources on his website, especially in relation to voice-hearing

Spiritual Crisis Network. www.spiritualcrisisnetwork.org.uk Offers an alternative perspective, practical advice and email support to people who are interested in exploring the idea of spiritual crisis.

The Council for Evidence-Based Psychiatry. www.cepuk.org Supporting the evaluation and use of the best evidence, and hosting articles and resources.

The Inner Compass. www.theinnercompass.org Extensive collection of resources about psychiatric drugs and how to withdraw from them.

The Open Paradigm Project. http://openparadigmproject.com A collection of video testimonies by people who have experienced various forms of madness, and their paths out of the mental health system.

The Voice Collective. http://www.voicecollective.co.uk Hosted by Mind in Camden, this is a resource 'for young people who hear, see and sense things others don't'.

The Voices in My Head. www.ted.com/talks/eleanor_longden_the_voices_ in_my_head A short TED talk in which psychologist and voice-hearer Eleanor Longden talks about her experiences.

Private therapy

Registered counsellors and therapists can be found through various directories, including:

BACP. www.bacp.co.uk/search/Therapists

Black African and Asian Therapy Network (BAATN). www.baatn.org.uk/ find-a-therapist

Counselling Directory. www.counselling-directory.org.uk

National Counselling Society. https://nationalcounsellingsociety.org/counsell ing-directory

UKCP. www.psychotherapy.org.uk/find-a-therapist

Clinical psychologists can be found through:

British Psychological Society. www.bps.org.uk/psychology-public/find-psychologist/find-psychologist

Appendix: General patterns

As explained in Chapter 8 of this book, the PTMF summarises common patterns that can be found across many people's individual stories. We have called these 'general patterns', and they are based on a great deal of evidence about the impact of power, threat, meaning and threat responses in people's lives. It can be reassuring to realise that other people have been through similar experiences and have reacted in similar ways. The general patterns may also help us to think about additional power, threat, meaning and threat response aspects of a personal story. This appendix contains a brief summary of the main features of all the general patterns, including the ones that were given as examples in Chapter 8.

For those who wish to read more, the general patterns are described in detail on pages 47–73 of the PTMF *Overview*, at www.bps.org.uk/PTM-Overview. Each general pattern also includes a number of sub-patterns, which describe common patterns of response to specific circumstances and situations, such domestic abuse, bullying, coping with childbirth, homelessness, being a refugee or asylum seeker and so on. These can also be found at the link above.

It is important to note that:

- The general patterns are not simple replacements for particular psychiatric diagnoses. They cut across diagnoses, and also include people with no diagnosis at all.

- Often there is no neat fit between a particular person and a particular general pattern. Many people will recognise parts of their story in several patterns.

- The general patterns are on a spectrum. The effects of power and threat on a particular person depend on many factors.

Some people will have much milder difficulties; others will have greater struggles.

- The general patterns will be amended and changed over time as more evidence emerges. In particular, we know less about typical patterns in non-Western cultures and settings in the UK and across the world.

The general pattern that we have called 'Identities' (below) is a useful starting point for everyone, since we all have aspects of our identity that influence the ways we respond to adversities and the impact of power.

Identities

Distress may be experienced by anyone, including those who have had more advantages and privileges in their lives. Everyone is impacted by the negative operation of power in one form or another, and higher social status sometimes involves its own particular pressures and adversities, such as being sent away to boarding school at a very young age or having to live up to high expectations of achievement. However, as a generalisation, some identities offer more protection in the form of greater power, status, control and access to social capital, along with more options for support, escape, safety and healing in the face of adversities. In addition, we all have several aspects of our identity, some of which may be less valued than others. For example, we may be female and middle class; male, gay and Black; able-bodied and poor, and so on. The devalued aspect(s) of our identity may relate to ethnicity, nationality, sexual orientation, age, gender identity, religion, or disability.

Having several marginalised aspects to our identity (for example, female, older and disabled) is likely to expose us to a greater degree of discrimination and increases the likelihood of experiencing other threats in our relationships and social circumstances, along with physical health problems. These are likely to include chronic background threats, such as living in deprived and unsafe environments or facing discrimination in pay and employment, education, housing, transport, healthcare and so on. Negative stereotypes of your group may lead to numerous examples of hostility and harassment and 'micro-aggressions', or multiple daily interactions that subtly disrespect individuals because of the group they belong to.

Ideological power is involved in creating meanings, identities, norms and standards against which group members' behaviour, characters and value may be judged negatively. Marginalised groups may face 'epistemic injustice', in which they are denied the opportunity to make sense of their own experiences in their own way due to unequal power relations and lack of shared social resources. All of this may occur in a context of historical and trans-generational oppression of a whole social or cultural group by, for example, warfare and colonisation, leading to losses of community bonds and of important forms of knowledge, rituals, practices or homeland.

It is also true that people may experience strong support within their particular group, even – or especially – if it is a marginalised one, and this may provide opportunities for resistance and the reclaiming of self-worth and positive identities. Meanings of exclusion, shame, humiliation, entrapment, inferiority, worthlessness, powerlessness, and injustice/unfairness can then be challenged, and threat responses that draw on skills, strengths, material, relational and social support, alternative narratives and other power resources may help to create social solidarity and awareness of ideological power, leading to social action.

As a general rule, all mental health diagnoses are more commonly applied in people with devalued identities, and this in itself sets the scene for further experiences of shame, failure, exclusion and re-traumatisation. For example, people from minority ethnic backgrounds living in the UK have much higher rates of all types of diagnosed mental health problems in proportion to their numbers. Being defined as 'mentally ill' tends to outweigh more positive aspects of your identity, so that even people with higher status are likely to experience discrimination and damage to their sense of self if they are psychiatrically diagnosed.

Surviving rejection, entrapment and invalidation

This pattern describes people's attempts to survive relationship threats of abuse, neglect and invalidation in situations where they were isolated, dependent and trapped. This may lead to core feelings/meanings of rejection, abandonment, shame, guilt, emptiness, powerlessness and meaninglessness. They may be fearful and distrusting, caught between a need to find and maintain safe relationships while protecting themselves from further rejection, hurt or harm. This dilemma frequently has its roots in early life, when there may have been sexual abuse and other traumas, such as bullying and witnessing domestic violence. Alternatively, or additionally, there may have been more subtle forms of emotional neglect, invalidation, criticism and control. There has often been re-traumatisation in adult life.

Gender socialisation shapes the way these threats are expressed. Women may be encouraged to direct anger inwards, leading to common threat responses of dissociation, low mood and self-injury. They may also have physical health problems. The pattern describes some women in the criminal justice system who report high levels of childhood abuse, domestic violence and rape, and who may self-harm and have unstable lives and relationships. They may be using illegal drugs to manage overwhelming feelings. Their male counterparts are, because of gender socialisation, more likely to be described by the general pattern 'Surviving social exclusion, shame, and coercive power'.

These survival patterns often originate in families that were struggling with their own relationship and social threats, which in turn are rooted in poverty, social inequality, discrimination, unemployment, gender inequalities and war.

The survival dilemmas described in this pattern may lead to being diagnosed with 'borderline personality disorder', 'bipolar disorder', 'dissociative disorder', 'major depressive disorder', 'PTSD', 'alcoholism', 'psychosis', and other such labels. The pattern may also describe people who have never received a formal diagnosis.

Surviving insecure attachments and adversities as a child/young person

This pattern describes a child's or young person's attempts to survive very difficult early relationships and environments, which may include neglect, abuse, violence or loss of parental figures. Sometimes there is an intergenerational history of trauma and adversity, made worse by poverty, lack of material resources, social marginalisation and isolation.

Gender socialisation means that boys are more likely to use threat responses such as hyperactivity, inattentiveness and aggression, while girls may be more likely to react with dissociation, self-harm, low mood and eating problems. Overwhelming feelings may be regulated by alcohol and illegal drugs. Depending on a child's age, there may be delays in reaching developmental milestones in speech, language and behaviour. There may also be physical health symptoms and conditions. Children may face multiple threats and commonly experience feelings/meanings such as shame, fear, worthlessness, distrust, rage, failure, abandonment, entrapment and hopelessness.

All these reactions take place in a wider power context of educational systems, social environments, racial and other forms of discrimination, and deprivation and socioeconomic inequalities, along with expectations of certain standards of behaviour and achievement. At an extreme, children and young people may be surviving organised abuse, war or refugee status.

The survival dilemmas described in this pattern may lead to being diagnosed with one or more of a whole range of conditions, including 'attachment disorder', 'ADHD', 'oppositional defiant disorder', 'depression', 'phobias' and 'anxiety disorders'. The pattern may also describe children who have not received a formal diagnosis.

Surviving separation and identity confusion

This pattern describes people's attempts to survive dilemmas about separation and identity, typically in early adulthood, although these challenges can emerge at any transition points in life, such as mid-life, retirement, or bereavement. The person faces a threat to their sense of self, identity and agency. There may be a struggle to find a balance between dependence/loss of self and autonomy/fear of abandonment. Other core meanings/feelings are rejection, worthlessness, failure, shame, inferiority, and feeling controlled, afraid, invaded or trapped. The person may respond with confusion, compliance, using rituals, perfectionism, and/or anger and rebellion.

In the case of young adults, families of origin may find it hard to offer support, due to their own trauma histories, lack of support or gender/cultural expectations. This may contribute to parental or carer attitudes of protection, control and/or criticism, along with confusing communication styles. All of this may be intensified in individualistic cultures with a strong emphasis on separation from the nuclear family in late teens/early 20s, coupled with high expectations about independence, striving, hard work, competitiveness and achievement.

The survival dilemmas described in this pattern may lead to being diagnosed with 'psychosis', 'schizophrenia', 'anorexia', 'bulimia', 'depression' and 'OCD', along with others. The pattern may also describe people who have never been formally diagnosed.

Surviving defeat, entrapment, disconnection and loss

This pattern describes people's attempts to survive feeling trapped in long-term situations of chronic stress, such as abusive relationships, or inescapable social environments, such as poverty, loneliness, social exclusion, unemployment, refugee status and so on. Sometimes there are childhood experiences of loss, abuse, criticism, bullying and neglect as well. People using this survival pattern are likely to experience core feelings/meanings of defeat, entrapment, isolation and loneliness, hopelessness and loss. Poor physical health or pain and disability may add to the person's difficulties, and they may feel a failure for not meeting social expectations of success. Threat responses may include low mood, exhaustion, giving up, self-blame, anxiety, or use of alcohol and drugs.

This pattern of distress is more common in less powerful groups: for example, female, low social class, older and/or ethnic minority. These are the groups who are the most likely to suffer the consequences of high unemployment, low wages, poor work conditions and so on. As with all the patterns, gender role expectations play a part. On the whole, women are more likely to be trapped in violent relationships or low status jobs, and to be carrying the main responsibility for childcare, while men are more likely to experience the trap of unemployment as a threat to their sense of identity and their place in the community.

At a broader level, the pattern shows how whole communities are impacted and fragmented by economic austerity, social inequality and injustice. This means that everyone, even those who are more affluent and protected, is likely to experience increased levels of feeling trapped and powerless, fear and distrust, isolation and loneliness, humiliation and shame and instability and insecurity.

The survival dilemma described in this pattern may lead to being diagnosed with 'depression', 'anxiety disorder', 'post-natal depression' or 'alcoholism'/'substance abuse', along with other possibilities. It may also describe people who have never received a formal diagnosis.

Surviving social exclusion, shame and coercive power

This describes the survival pattern of someone who is likely to have faced threat, discrimination, material deprivation and social exclusion in their early life, both inside and outside the family. This may have included having an absent father, being in institutional care, and homelessness. Parents and caregivers may have been struggling with their own histories of adversity, past and present, often by using drugs and alcohol. As a result, the person's early relationships were often disrupted and insecure, and they may have experienced significant traumas as a child and as an adult, including physical and sexual abuse, bullying, witnessing domestic violence and harsh or humiliating parenting styles. Being sent to institutions like prison or a psychiatric hospital may multiply the experience of threat. All of this may lead the person to experience core feelings/meanings of worthlessness, inferiority, powerlessness, shame, rejection and a sense of injustice. A variation of this pattern may arise in more privileged circumstances when young children are sent away to boarding school.

To cope with this, people often use survival strategies of cutting off from their own and others' emotions, maintaining emotional distance, distrust, remaining highly alert to threat, and sometimes defending against pain and humiliation by anger and violence. They may also suppress their feelings with drugs and alcohol. These responses are shaped in men by socialisation to direct their anger and pain outwards. 'Paranoia', or suspicious thoughts, is also common, and is linked especially in minority ethnic groups to actual experiences of discrimination, racism and exclusion.

These patterns are more likely to occur in economically unequal societies, in which people have to compete for jobs, resources and symbols of achievement and material success. These pressures affect women and men slightly differently, due to gender-role expectations. Men generally face greater pressure to compete, achieve and maintain high social status, which means that, in an unequal society, disadvantaged men may face constant humiliating reminders of their failure to do this.

The survival dilemmas described in this pattern may lead to being diagnosed with paranoia. A common diagnosis in men is 'anti-social personality disorder' or 'substance abuse'. Women using these survival strategies are more likely to be labelled with 'borderline personality disorder' or 'bipolar disorder'. The pattern may also describe people who have never been formally diagnosed.

Surviving single threats

This pattern describes common ways of surviving single abuses of power, such as rape or threats in war and combat. These major threats can occur on their own, as well as part of other general patterns. Victims of rape typically experience terror, humiliation and powerlessness, and feelings/meanings of blame, shame and guilt. Threat responses include low mood, anxiety, panic, hypervigilance, avoidance and the use of drugs or alcohol. Because of gender socialisation, men tend to create slightly different meanings than women. Combat may leave people with hyperarousal, intrusive memories and flashbacks, numbing, insomnia and so on. As with traumatic events in general, the impact may be shaped by previous histories of trauma and by wider social meanings – for example, a sense of injustice if a rape case is unsuccessful, or a sense of betrayal if a war is felt to be unjustified. The survival dilemmas described in this pattern are commonly diagnosed as 'PTSD'. Healing may be found through engagement, solidarity and shared meanings with other victims.

References

Adegoke, Y. (2020, February 26). 'I'm happy to announce…': How we entered a great big era of boastfulness. *The Guardian*. www.theguardian.com/media/commentisfree/2020/feb/26/im-happy-to-announce-how-we-entered-a-great-big-era-of-boastfulness

American Psychiatric Association. (2013). *Diagnostic and statistical manual of mental disorders* (5th Ed.). American Psychiatric Association.

Anda, R. F., Brown, D. W., Felitti, V. J., Bremner, J. D., Dube, S. R., & Giles, W. H. (2007). Adverse childhood experiences and prescribed psychotropic medications in adults. *American Journal of Preventative Medicine, 32*, 389–394.

Barber, B. R. (2007). *How Markets Corrupt Children, Infantalise Adults and Swallow Citizens Whole.* Norton.

Barnwell, G., Stroud, L., & Watson, M. (2020). Critical reflections from South Africa: Using the Power Threat Meaning Framework to place climate related distress in its sociopolitical context. *Clinical Psychology Forum, 332* (August), 7–15.

Barrett, R.J. (2004). Kurt Schneider in Borneo: Do first rank symptoms apply to the Iban? In J.H. Jenkins & R.J. Barrett (Eds.), *Schizophrenia, culture and subjectivity: The edge of experience* (pp.87–109). Cambridge University Press.

Bates, L. (2014). *Everyday sexism.* Simon & Schuster.

BBC News, (2016, February 29). Black MP was 'mistaken for a cleaner' in Westminster. *BBC News.*

Belluck., P. & Carey, B. (2013, May 6). Psychiatry's guide is out of touch with science, experts say. *New York Times*. http://www.nytimes.com/2013/05/07/health/psychiatrys-new-guide-falls-short-experts-say.html?pagewanted=all&_r=0

Bender, M. (2019). Notes on 'Operation Fear'. *Clinical Psychology Forum, 324* (December), 42-46.

Bennett, M. R., & Hacker, P. M. S. (2003). *Philosophical foundations of neuroscience.* Blackwells.

Beresford, P. (2016). The role of survivor evidence in creating alternatives to psychiatry. In J. Russo & A. Sweeney (eds.), *Searching for a rose garden: Challenging psychiatry, fostering mad studies* (pp. 25-34). PCCS Books.

Beresford, P., Perring, R., Nettle, M., & Wallcraft, J. (2016). *From mental illness to a social model of madness and distress*. Shaping Our Lives.

Berlant, L. (2011). *Cruel optimism*. Duke University Press.

Billig, M. (1996). *Arguing and thinking. A rhetorical approach to social psychology* (2nd ed.). Cambridge University Press.

Boyle, M. (1997). *Rethinking abortion: Psychology, gender, power and the law*. Routledge.

Boyle, M. (1999). Diagnosis. In C. Newnes., G. Holmes & C. Dunn (eds.), *This is madness: A critical look at psychiatry and the future of mental health services* (pp. 75-90). PCCS Books.

Boyle, M. (2002a). *Schizophrenia: A scientific delusion?* (2nd ed.). Routledge.

Boyle, M. (2002b). It's all done with smoke and mirrors. Or, how to create the illusion of a schizophrenic brain disorder. *Clinical Psychology, 12*, 9-16.

Boyle, M. (2011). Making the world go away, and how psychology and psychiatry benefit. In M. Rapley, J. Moncrieff & J. Dillon (eds.). *De-medicalising misery: Psychiatry, psychology and the human condition* (pp 27-43). Palgrave Macmillan.

Boyle, M. (2013). The persistence of medicalisation: Is the presentation of alternatives part of the problem? In S. Coles, S. Keenan & B. Diamond (eds.). *Madness contested: Power and practice* (pp. 3-22). PCCS Books.

Bracken, P. (2002). *Trauma: Culture, meaning and philosophy*. John Wiley & Sons

Cameron, J., Hart, A., Brooker, S., Neale, P., & Reardon, M. (2018). Collaboration in the design and delivery of a mental health recovery college course. *Journal of Mental Health, 27*, 374-381.

Carr, E. M. (2020, January 15). Gaslighting: Should we label the victims as psychotic or abused? *Mad in the UK*. www.madintheuk.com/2020/01/gaslighting-label-victims-psychotic-or-abused

Chase, E., & Walker, R. (2012). The co-construction of shame in the context of poverty: Beyond a threat to the social bond. *Sociology, 47*(4), 739-754.

Cohen, B. (2016). *Psychiatric hegemony: a Marxist theory of mental illness*. Palgrave Macmillan.

Collins, N. (2019). The 'own my life' course: Building literacy with women about trauma through the Power Threat Meaning Framework. *Clinical Psychology Forum, 313*, 38-41.

Commission on Social Determinants of Health. (2008). *CSDH final report: Closing the gap in a generation: Health equity through action on the social determinants of health*. World Health Organization.

Cosgrove, L., & Wheeler, E. E. (2013). Industry's colonization of psychiatry: Ethical and practical implications of financial conflicts of interest in the DSM-5. *Feminism & Psychology, 23*, 3–9.

Costa, L., Voronka, J., Landry, D., Reid, J. (2012). Recovering our stories: A small act of resistance. *Studies in Social Justice, 5*(1), 85–101.

Crenshaw, K. (1989). Demarginalizing the intersection of race and sex: A black feminist critique of antidiscrimination doctrine, feminist theory and antiracist politics. *University of Chicago Legal Forum, 140*, 139–167.

Cromby, J. (2015). *Feeling bodies: Embodying psychology*. Palgrave Macmillan.

Daley, P. (2020, March 24). We face a pandemic of mental health disorders. Those who do it hardest need our support. *The Guardian*. www.theguardian.com/commentisfree/2020/mar/25/we-face-a-pandemic-of-mental-health-disorders-those-who-do-it-hardest-need-our-support

Davidson, L., & McGlashan, T. (1997). The varied outcomes of schizophrenia. *Canadian Journal of Psychiatry, 42*, 34–43.

Davies, J. (2013). *Cracked: Why psychiatry is doing more harm than good*. Icon Books.

Davies, J., & Read, J. (2019). A systematic review into the incidence, severity and duration of antidepressant withdrawal effects: Are guidelines evidence based? *Addictive Behaviours, 97*, 111–121.

Delano, L. (2013). Reflections on a psychiatric indoctrination, or, how I began to free myself from the cult of psychiatry. *Mad in America*. www.madinamerica.com/2013/02/reflections-on-a-psychiatric-indoctrination-or-how-i-began-to-free-myself-from-the-cult-of-psychiatry

Dillon, J. (2016, May 10). The psychological is political. *YouTube*. www.youtube.com/watch?v=cQ4fSa18de8

Dillon, J. & May, R. (2003). Reclaiming experiences. *Openmind 120*, 16–17.

Division of Clinical Psychology. (2013). *Classification of Behaviour and Experience in Relation to Functional Psychiatric Diagnoses: Time for a paradigm shift*. British Psychological Society. www.bps.org.uk/sites/www.bps.org.uk/files/Member%20Networks/Divisions/DCP/Classification%20of%20behaviour%20and%20experience%20in%20relation%20to%20functional%20psychiatric%20diagnoses.pdf

Eaton, J. (2019*). 'Logically I know I am not to blame, but I still feel to blame': Exploring and measuring the victim blaming and self-blame of women who* *have been subjected to sexual violence.* [Thesis]. University of Derby. https://doi.org/10.13140/RG.2.2.12986.95682

Eddo-Lodge, R. (2018). *Why I'm no longer talking to white people about race.* Bloomsbury.

Fernando, S. (2010). *Mental health, race and culture* (3rd ed.). Palgrave Macmillan.

Fine, C. (2011). *Delusions of gender: The real science behind sex differences.* Icon Books.

Flynn, A., & Polak, N. (2019). Incorporating the Power Threat Meaning Framework into an autism and learning disability team. *Clinical Psychology Forum, 313*, 42–46.

Francis, A. (2013). *Saving normal: An insider's revolt against out-of-control psychiatric diagnosis, DSM-5, big pharma and the medicalization of ordinary life.* Harper Collins.

Fricker, M. (2007). *Epistemic injustice: power and the ethics of knowing.* Oxford University Press.

Friedli, L., & Stearn, R. (2015). Positive affect as coercive strategy: Conditionality, activation and the role of psychology in the UK government workfare programmes. *Medical Humanities, 41*, 40–47.

Fromene, R., Guerin, B., & Krieg, A. (2014). Australian indigenous clients with a borderline personality disorder diagnosis: A contextual review. *The Psychological Record, 64*, 559–567.

Frost, L. (2016). Exploring the concepts of recognition and shame for social work. *Journal of Social Work Practice, 30*(4), 431–446.

Gerada, C. (2018, June 6). For doctors with mental illness, 'help me' can be the hardest words. *The Guardian.* www.theguardian.com/commentisfree/2018/jun/06/doctors-mental-health-problems-taboo

Goldacre, B. (2012). *Bad pharma: How drug companies mislead doctors and harm patients.* Fourth Estate.

Grant, A. (2015). Demedicalising misery: Welcoming the human paradigm in mental health nurse education. *Nurse Education Today, 35*, 50–53.

Griffiths, A. (2019). Reflections on using the Power Threat Meaning Framework in peer-led systems. *Clinical Psychology Forum, 313*, 25–32.

Hagan, T., & Donnison, J. (1999). Social power: Some implications for the theory and practice of cognitive behaviour therapy. *Journal of Community & Applied Social Psychology, 9*, 119–135.

Harewood, D. (Presenter). (2019, May 5). Psychosis and me. [Television documentary.] BBC 2. www.facebook.com/bbc/videos/racism-and-psychosis-david-harewood-psychosis-and-me/2281706492043368

Hari, J. (2018). *Lost connections: Why you're depressed and how to find hope.* Bloomsbury.

Harper, D., & Moss, D. (2003). A different kind of chemistry? Reformulating 'formulation'. *Clinical Psychology, 25,* 6–10.

Harper, D., & Thompson, A. R. (eds.). (2012). *Qualitative research methods in mental health and psychotherapy: A guide for students and practitioners.* Wiley Blackwell.

Harper, D. J. (2020). Framing, filtering and hermeneutical injustice in the public conversation about mental health. *Journal of Constructivist Psychology.* https://doi.org/10.1080/10720537.2020.1773360

Harvey, F. (2020, February 6). Humanity under threat from perfect storm of crises – study. *The Guardian.* www.theguardian.com/environment/2020/feb/06/humanity-under-threat-perfect-storm-crises-study-environment

Henderson, L. (2019). Popular television and public mental health: Creating media entertainment from mental distress. *Critical Public Health, 28,* 106–117.

Henriques, G. (2017, May 23). Twenty billion fails to 'move the needle' on mental illness. *Psychology Today.* www.psychologytoday.com/gb/blog/theory-knowledge/201705/twenty-billion-fails-move-the-needle-mental-illness

Herman, J. (1992). *Trauma and recovery: The aftermath of violence – from domestic abuse to political terror.* Basic Books.

Herrero, J., Torres, A., Rodríguez, F. J., & Juarros-Basterretxea, J. (2017). Intimate partner violence against women in the European Union: The influence of male partners' traditional gender roles and general violence. *Psychology of Violence, 7*(3), 385–394.

Holmes, S., Drake, S., Odgers, K., & Wilson, J. (2017). *Feminist approaches to anorexia nervosa: A qualitative study of a treatment group. Journal of Eating Disorders, 5, 36.* https://ueaeprints.uea.ac.uk/id/eprint/64112/4/Published_manuscript.pdf

Hornstein, G. (2012). *Agnes's jacket: A psychologist's search for the meanings of madness.* PCCS Books.

Horwitz, A. V. (2010). How an age of anxiety became an age of depression. *The Milbank Quarterly, 88(1),* 112–138

Insel, T. (2013, April 29). Post by former NIMH director Thomas Insel: Transforming diagnosis. *National Institute of Mental Health.* www.nimh.nih.gov/about/director/2013/transforming-diagnosis.shtml

Ireland, C. (2009, March 19). Fijian girls succumb to western dysmorphia. *Harvard Gazette.* https://news.harvard.edu/gazette/story/2009/03/fijian-girls-succumb-to-western-dysmorphia

Jacobs, D. H., & Cohen, D. (2010). Does 'psychological dysfunction' mean anything? A critical essay on pathology versus agency. *The Journal of Humanistic Psychology, 50*, 312–334.

Janssen, I., Krabbendam, L., Bak, M., Hanssen, M., Vollebergh, W., de Graaf, R., van Os, J. (2004). Childhood abuse as a risk factor for psychotic experiences. *Acta Psychiatrica Scandinavica, 109*, 38–45.

Jetten, J., Haslam, C. & Haslam, S.A. (2012). *The social cure: Identity, health and well-being.* Hove: Psychology Press.

Johnson, S. (2018, November 22). 'I felt so worthless': Two teenagers on their mental health struggles. *The Guardian.* www.theguardian.com/society/2018/nov/22/i-felt-so-worthless-two-teenagers-on-their-mental-health-struggles

Johnston, J. (1974). *Lesbian nation: The feminist solution.* Simon & Schuster.

Johnstone, L. (2000). *Users and abusers of psychiatry: A critical look at psychiatric practice.* (2nd ed.). Brunner-Routledge.

Johnstone, L. (2014). *A straight talking introduction to psychiatric diagnosis.* PCCS Books.

Johnstone, L. (2020a, September 3). Does coronavirus pose a challenge to the diagnoses of anxiety and depression? A psychologist's view. *BJPsych Bulletin.* DOI: 10.1192/bjb.2020.101

Johnstone, L. (2020b, April 7). We are all in this together. *Mad in America.* www.madintheuk.com/2020/04/we-are-all-in-this-together

Johnstone, L., & Boyle, M., with Cromby, J., Dillon, J., Harper, D., Kinderman, P., Longden, E., Pilgrim, D., & Read, J. (2018a). *The Power Threat Meaning Framework: Towards the identification of patterns in emotional distress, unusual experiences and troubled or troubling behaviour, as an alternative to functional psychiatric diagnosis.* British Psychological Society. www.bps.org.uk/power-threat-meaning-framework

Johnstone, L., & Boyle, M., with Cromby, J., Dillon, J., Harper, D., Kinderman, P., Longden, E., Pilgrim, D., & Read, J. (2018b). *The Power Threat Meaning Framework: Overview.* British Psychological Society.

Johnstone, L., Boyle, M., Cromby, C., Dillon, J., Harper, D., Kinderman, P., Longden, E., Pilgrim, D., & Read, R. (2019). Reflections on responses to the Power Threat Meaning Framework one year on. *Clinical Psychology Forum, 313*, 47–54.

Johnstone, L., & Dallos, R. (eds.). (2013). *Formulation in psychology and psychotherapy: Making sense of people's problems* (2nd ed.). Brunner-Routledge.

Johnstone, L., & Kopua, D. (2019). Crossing cultures with the Power Threat Meaning Framework. *Psychotherapy and Politics International, 17*, 2.

Jones, O. (2020, January 16). Male rape survivors suffer in silence. We need to help them talk. *The Guardian.*

Joseph, J. (2015, January 5). Quotations from the genetics 'graveyard': nearly half a century of false positive gene discovery claims in psychiatry. Mad in America. www.madinamerica.com/2015/01/quotations-genetics-graveyard-nearly-half-century-of-false-positive-gene-discovery-claims-psychiatry

Joseph, J. (2020, June 21). It's time to abandon the 'classical twin method' in behavioral research. The Gene Illusion in Behavioural Research. https://thegeneillusion.blogspot.com/2020/06/its-time-to-abandon-classical-twin_21.html

Kanter, J., & Manbeck, K. (2020, April 3). COVID-19 could lead to an epidemic of clinical depression, and the healthcare system isn't ready for that either. *The Conversation.* https://theconversation.com/covid-19-could-lead-to-an-epidemic-of-clinical-depression-and-the-health-care-system-isnt-ready-for-that-either-134528

Kelly, L., Lovett, J., & Regan, L. (2005). A gap or a chasm? Attrition rates in reported rape cases. *Home Office Research Study 293.* The Home Office.

Kirk, S. A., Gomory, T., & Cohen, D. (2013). *Mad science: Psychiatric coercion, diagnosis and drugs.* Transaction Publishers.

Kirk, S. A., & Kutchins, H. (1992). *The selling of DSM: The rhetoric of science in psychiatry.* Aldine de Gruyter.

Kupfer, D. (2013, May 3). Chair of DSM-5 Task Force discusses future of mental health research. [News release.] *American Psychiatric Association.*

Kutchins, H., & Kirk, S. A. (1997). *Making us crazy. DSM: The psychiatric bible and the creation of mental disorders.* The Free Press.

Kvaale, E., Haslam, N., & Gottdiener, W. (2013). The 'side effects' of medicalization: A meta-analytic review of how biogenetic explanations affect stigma. *Clinical Psychology Review, 53,* 782–794.

Leeming, D., Boyle, M., & Macdonald, J. (2009). Accounting for psychological problems. How user-friendly are psychosocial formulations? *Clinical Psychology Forum, 200,* 12–17.

Leising, D., Roger, K., & Ostner, J. (2009). The undisordered personality: Normative assumptions underlying personality disorder diagnoses. *Review of General Psychology, 13*(3), 230–241.

Leo, J., & Lacasse, J. R. (2008). The media and the chemical imbalance theory of depression. *Society, 4,* 35–45.

Lieberman, J., & First, M. (2007). Renaming schizophrenia. *British Medical Journal, 334,* 108.

Littlewood, R., & Lipsedge, M. (1997). *Aliens and alienists: Ethnic minorities and psychiatry.* (3rd ed.). Routledge.

Longden, E. (2017). Listening to the voices people hear: Auditory hallucinations beyond a diagnostic framework. *Journal of Humanistic Psychology, 57*(6), 573–601.

Longden, E., Corstens, D., Escher, S., & Romme, M. (2012). Voice hearing in biographical context: A model for formulating the relationship between voices and life history. *Psychosis, 4*, 224–234.

Mauthner, N. S. (2010). Women's narratives of post-partum depression. In D. C. Jack & A. Ali (eds.). *Silencing the self across cultures: Depression and gender in the social world* (pp. 459–484). Oxford University Press.

McFetridge, M. A., Milner, R., Gavin, V., & Levita, L. (2015). Borderline personality disorder: Patterns of self-harm, reported childhood trauma and clinical outcome. *British Journal of Psychiatry Open, 1*(1), 18–20.

McGruder, J.H. (2004). Madness in Zanzibar: An exploration of lived experience. J.H. Jenkins & R.J. Barrett (Eds.), *Schizophrenia, culture and subjectivity: The edge of experience* (pp.255–281). Cambridge University Press.

McInerney, L. (2019, December 17). British girls have finally made the global top table… for fear of failure. How terrifying. *The Guardian*. www.theguardian.com/education/2019/dec/17/british-girls-fear-of-failure-pisa-ranking

Mead, S., & Filson, B. (2016). Becoming part of each other's narratives: Intentional Peer Support. In J. Russo & A. Sweeney (eds.), *Searching for a rose garden: Challenging psychiatry, fostering mad studies* (pp. 109–117). PCCS Books.

Metzl, J. M. (2010). *The protest psychosis: How schizophrenia became a black disease*. Beacon Press.

Midlands Psychology Group. (2013). Manifesto for a social materialist psychology of distress. In S. Coles, S. Keenan & B. Diamond. (eds.), *Madness Contested: Power and practice* (pp. 121–140). PCCS Books.

Mills, C., & Fernando, S. (2014). Globalising mental health or pathologising the global south? Mapping the ethics, theory and practice of global mental health. *Disability and the Global South, 1*, 188–202.

Moffatt, S., Lawson, S., Patterson, R., Holding, E., Dennison, A., Sowden, S., & Brown, J. (2016). A qualitative study of the impact of the UK 'bedroom tax'. *Journal of Public Health, 38*, 197–205.

Moncrieff, J. (2008a). *The myth of the chemical cure: A critique of psychiatric drug treatment*. Palgrave Macmillan.

Moncrieff, J. (2008b). Neoliberalism and biopsychiatry: a marriage of convenience. In: C.I. Cohen & S. Timimi (eds.). *Liberatory psychiatry, philosophy, politics and mental health* (pp. 235–256). Cambridge University Press.

Moncrieff, J. (2013). *The bitterest pills: The troubling story of antipsychotic drugs.* Palgrave Macmillan.

Moncrieff, J. (2013, November 21). *Models of drug action.* https://joannamoncrieff.com/2013/11/21/models-of-drug-action

Moncrieff, J. (2020). *A straight talking introduction to psychiatric drugs: The truth about how they work and how to come off them.* (2nd ed.). PCCS Books.

Morrill, Z. (2019, March 18). It is time to challenge the candidate-gene approach to depression. *Mad In America.* www.madinamerica.com/2019/03/time-abandon-search-genetic-underpinnings-depression/

Newnham, E. A., & Janca, A. (2014). Childhood adversity and borderline personality disorder: A focus on adolescence. *Current Opinion in Psychiatry, 27*(1), 68–72.

Newton, J. (2013). *Preventing mental Ill-health.* Routledge.

New Zealand Government Inquiry into Mental Health and Addiction. (2018). *Government inquiry into mental health and addiction.* https://mentalhealth.inquiry.govt.nz/inquiry-report/he-ara-oranga/executive-summary

NHS Digital. (2018). *Mental health of children and young people in England, 2017.* https://digital.nhs.uk/data-and-information/publications/statistical/mental-health-of-children-and-young-people-in-england/2017/2017

O'Grady, H. (2005). *Woman's relationship with herself. Gender, Foucault and therapy.* Routledge.

Office of the High Commissioner for Human Rights. (2017). *Report of the Special Rapporteur on the right of everyone to the enjoyment of the highest attainable standard of physical and mental health.* United Nations.

Office of the High Commissioner for Human Rights. (2019). *Removing obstacles to liveable lives: A rights-based approach to suicide prevention*. Open Statement by the Special Rapporteur on the right of everyone to the enjoyment of the highest attainable standard of physical and mental health. United Nations. www.ohchr.org/EN/NewsEvents/Pages/DisplayNews.aspx?NewsID=25117&LangID=E

Orbach, S. (1978). *Fat is a Feminist Issue: The anti-diet guide to permanent weight loss.* Paddington Press.

Orbach, S. (2019, August 23). Will this be the last generation to have bodies that are familiar to us? *The Guardian.* www.theguardian.com/books/2019/aug/23/susie-orbach-that-will-bodies-be-like-in-the-future

Patterson, C., Tyler, C., Lexmond, J. (2014). *Character and resilience manifesto.* All Party Parliamentary Group on Social Mobility.

Randall, J., Johnson, E., & Johnstone, L, (2020). Self-formulation: Making sense of your own experiences. In J. Randall (ed.), *Surviving clinical psychology: Navigating personal, professional and political selves on the journey to qualification* (pp. 142–164). Routledge.

Read, J. (2005). The bio-bio-bio model of madness. *The Psychologist, 18,* 596-597. https://thepsychologist.bps.org.uk/volume-18/edition-10/bio-bio-bio-model-madness

Read, J. (2010). Can poverty drive you mad? 'Schizophrenia', socio-economic-status and the case for primary prevention. *New Zealand Journal of Psychology, 39,* 7–19.

Read, J. (2016, October 24). Hearing voices is like saying hello to your family. *The Independent.* www.independent.co.uk/life-style/health-and-families/hearing-voices-is-normal-a7377426.html

Read, J. (2018, May 1). UK Royal College dismisses complaint. *Mad in America.* www.madinamerica.com/2018/05/royal-college-dismisses-complaint

Read, J., Bentall, R. P., & Fosse, R. (2009). Time to abandon the bio-bio-bio model of psychosis: Exploring the epigenetic and psychological mechanisms by which adverse life events lead to psychotic symptoms. *Epidemiologica e Psichiatria Sociale, 18,* 299–317.

Read, J., Haslam, N., & Magliano, L. (2013). Prejudice, stigma and 'schizophrenia': The role of biogenetic ideology. In J. Read & J. Dillon (eds.), *Models of madness: Psychological, social and biological approaches to psychosis.* (2nd ed.) (pp. 157–177). Routledge.

Read, J., van Os, J., Morrison, A. P., & Ross, C. A. (2005). Childhood trauma, psychosis and schizophrenia: A literature review and clinical implications. *Acta Psychiatrica Scandinavica, 112,* 330–350.

Regier, D. A., Narrow, W. E., Clarke, D. E., Kraemer, H. C., Kuramoto, S. J., Kuhl, E. A., Kupfer, D. J. (2013). DSM-5 field trials in the United States and Canada, Part II: Test-retest reliability of selected categorical diagnoses. *American Journal of Psychiatry, 170,* 59–70.

Reis, M., Dinelli, S., & Elias, L. (2019). Surviving prison: Using the Power Threat Meaning Framework to explore the impact of long-term imprisonment. *Clinical Psychology Forum, 313,* 25–32.

Rippon, G. (2020). *The gendered brain.* Vintage.

Robertson, I. (2013). The winner effect gone bad: The problem of hubris in leadership. *The Psychologist 26*(3), 186–189.

Rosen, C., Jones, N., Longden, E., Chase, K. A., Shattell, M., Melbourne, J. K., Keedy, S. K., & Sharma, R. P. (2017). Exploring the intersections of trauma, structural adversity, and psychosis among a primarily African-American sample: A mixed-methods analysis. *Frontier Psychiatry 8*(57). https://doi.org/10.3389/fpsyt.2017.00057

Salter, M. (2012). Invalidation: A neglected dimension of gender-based violence and inequality. *International Journal for Crime and Justice, 1,* 3–13.

Scull, A. T. (1979). *Museums of madness: The social organisation of insanity in 19th century England.* Allen Lane.

Sharfstein, S. (2005, August 19). Big pharma and American psychiatry: the good, the bad and the ugly. *Psychiatric News.* https://doi.org/10.1176/pn.40.16.00400003

Shevlin, M., McAnee, G., Bentall, R.P. & Murphy, J. (2015). Specificity of association between adversities and the occurrence and co-occurrence of paranoia and hallucinations: Evaluating the stability of childhood risk in an adverse adult environment. *Psychosis 7*(3), 206–216.

SHIFT Recovery Community. (2020, June 8). Using the Power Threat Meaning Framework in a self-help group of people with experience of mental and emotional distress. *Journal of Constructivist Psychology.*

Shotter, J. (1993). *Cultural politics of everyday life.* Open University Press.

Sigman, M. (2019). *The secret life of the mind: How our brain thinks, feels and decides.* William Collins.

Simons, P. (2020, September 16). Mental health apps: A1 surveillance enters our world. *Mad in America.* www.madinamerica.com/2020/03/mental-health-apps-ai-surveillance/?mc_cid=111294bd1e&mc_eid=0adfedd9d6

Smail, D. (2005). *Power, interest and psychology: Elements of a social materialist understanding of distress.* PCCS Books.

Snapes, L. (2020, January 24). Taylor Swift discloses fight with eating disorder in new documentary. *The Guardian.* www.theguardian.com/music/2020/jan/24/taylor-swift-eating-disorder-miss-americana-documentary-sundance-film-festival-lana-wilson

Spence, D.P. (1982). *Narrative truth and historical truth: Meaning and interpretation in psychoanalysis.* Norton.

Stanko, B., Norman, J., & Wunsch, D. (2007). *The attrition of rape allegations in London: A Review.* Metropolitan Police.

Stoppard, J. M. (2000). *Understanding depression: feminist social constructionist approaches.* Routledge.

Swami, V. (2019). 'Dads get sad too'. *The Psychologist, 32,* 28–32.

Sweeney, A. (2016) The transformative potential of survivor research. In J. Russo & A. Sweeney (eds.), *Searching for a Rose Garden: Challenging psychiatry, fostering mad studies* (pp. 49–58). PCCS Books.

Sweeney, A., Clement, S., Filson, B., & Kennedy, A. (2016). Trauma-informed mental healthcare in the UK: What is it and how can we further its development? *Mental Health Review Journal, 21*(3), 174–192.

Sweeney, A., & Taggart, D. (2018). (Mis)understanding trauma-informed approaches in mental health, *Journal of Mental Health, 27*(5), 383–387.

Tay, L. & Diener, E. (2011). Needs and subjective well-being around the world. *Journal of Personality and Social Psychology 101*(2), 354–365.

The Philadelphia ACE Project. (n.d.). *Philadelphia ACE survey. http://www. philadelphiaaces.org/philadelphia-ace-survey*

The Wisdom Collector. (2020, April 5). *The coronavirus crisis can teach us the need to reconnect.* https://thewisdomcollector.blogspot.com/2020/04/the-coronavirus-crisis-can-teach-us.html

Timimi, S. (2009). *A straight-talking introduction to children's mental health problems.* PCCS Books.

Timimi, S. (2011). Medicalising masculinity. In M. Rapley, J. Moncrieff & J. Dillon (eds.). *De-medicalising misery: Psychiatry, psychology and the human condition* (pp. 86–98). Palgrave Macmillan.

Timimi, S. (2014). No more psychiatric labels: Why formal psychiatric diagnostic systems should be abolished. *International Journal of Clinical and Health Psychology*, 14(3), 208–215.

Tirado, L. (2014). *Hand to mouth: The truth about being poor in a wealthy world.* Virago.

Turner, A. (2019, January 29). Good intentions but the right approach? *Public Healthy.* http://publichealthy.co.uk/good-intentions-but-the-right-approach-the-case-of-aces

UNFPA. (n.d.). *Gender-based violence.* United Nations Population Fund. http://www.unfpa.org/gender-based-violence#sthash.U28ff3vk.dpuf

Unsworth, E. J. (2019, June 8). 'It took months for me to accept a diagnosis for the pain and outrage I felt'. *The Guardian.* www.theguardian.com/ society/2019/jun/08/lie-health-visitor-lie-friends-truth-postnatal-depression

Usborne, S. (2019, October 10). Domestic murderers are often likeable men – that's how they have been able to abuse women. *The Guardian.* www. theguardian.com/lifeandstyle/2019/oct/10/domestic-murderers-are-often-likable-men-thats-how-they-have-been-able-to-abuse-women

Ussher, J. M. (2004). Premenstrual syndrome and self-policing: Ruptures in self-silencing leading to increased self-surveillance and blaming of the body. *Social Theory & Health, 2,* 254–272.

Ussher, J. M. (2011). *The madness of women: Myth and experience.* Routledge.

van der Kolk, B. (2014). *The body keeps the score: Mind, brain and body in the transformation of trauma*. Viking.

van der Zee, B. (2019, October 24). Is trauma handed down through generations? *The Guardian*. www.theguardian.com/society/2019/oct/24/is-trauma-handed-down-through-generations-ptsd-conflict

Varese, F., Smeets, F., Drukker, M., Lieverse, R., Lataster, T., Viechtbauer, W., Read, J., van Os, J., & Bentall, R. P. (2012). Childhood trauma increases the risk of psychosis: A meta-analysis of patient-control, prospective and cross-sectional cohort studies. *Schizophrenia Bulletin, 381*, 661–671.

Verhaeghe, P. (2014). *'What about Me?' The struggle for identity in a market-based society*. (J. Hedley-Prôle, Trans). Scribe Publications.

Wainberg, M.L., Scorza, P., Shultz, J.M., Helpman, L., Mootz, J.J., Johnson, K., Neria, Y., Bradford, J-M.E., Oquendo, M.A. & Arbuckle, M.R. (2017). Challenges and opportunities in global mental health: a research-to-practice perspective. *Current Psychiatry Reports 19*(28). https://doi.org/10.1007/s11920-017-0780-z

Wallcraft, J., Schrank, B., & Amering, M. (eds.). (2009). *Handbook of service user involvement in mental health research*. World Psychiatric Association. Wiley-Blackwell.

Warner, R. (2004). *Recovery from schizophrenia: Psychiatry and political economy* (3rd ed.). Brunner-Routledge.

Watters, E. (2011). *Crazy like us: The globalization of the Western mind*. Robinson.

Whitaker, R. (2011). *Anatomy of an epidemic: Magic bullets, psychiatric drugs, and the astonishing rise of mental illness in America*. Broadway Books.

Wilkinson, R., & Pickett, K. (2010). *The spirit level: Why equality is better for everyone*. Allen Lane.

Wilkinson, R., & Pickett, K. (2018). *The inner level: How more equal societies reduce stress, restore sanity and improve everyone's well-being*. Allen Lane.

Woodbury, Z. (2019). Climate trauma: Toward a new taxonomy of trauma. *Ecopsychology, 11*(1), 1–9. https://doi.org/10.1089/eco.2018.0021

World Health Organization [WHO]. (2019). *The International Classification of Diseases (11th ed)*. World Health Organization.

Wyllie, C., Platt, S., Brownlie, J., Chandler, A., Connolly, S., Evans, R., Kennelly, B., Kirtley, O., Moore, G., O'Connor, R., Scourfield, J. (2012). *Men, suicide and society: Why disadvantaged men in mid-life die by suicide*. Samaritans. https://media.samaritans.org/documents/Samaritans_MenSuicideSociety_ResearchReport2012.pdf

Name index

Subject index

Also by PCCS Books

The *Straight Talking Introductions* series
edited by Richard Bentall and Pete Sanders

*A Straight Talking Introduction to Psychiatric Drugs:
the truth about how they work and how to come off them*
Joanna Moncrieff

A Straight Talking Introduction to Psychiatric Diagnosis
Lucy Johnstone

*A Straight Talking Introduction to the Causes of
Mental Health Problems*
John Read and Pete Sanders

*A Straight Talking Introduction to Children's
Mental Health Problems*
Sami Timimi

*A Straight Talking Introduction to Being a
Mental Health Service User*
Peter Beresford

*A Straight Talking Introduction to Caring for Someone with
Mental Health Problems*
Jen Kilyon and Theresa Smith

**Available at discounted prices with free UK postage from
www.pccs-books.co.uk**

Also by PCCS Books

*Psychiatry and Mental Health:
A guide for counsellors and
psychotherapists*

Rachel Freeth
pp. 602

ISBN
paperback – 978 1 910919 52 1
epub – 978 1 910919 55 2

Increasingly, counsellors and psychotherapists are working with people who have been diagnosed with a mental disorder and are required to understand and navigate the mental health system. Counselling training rarely covers the fields of psychiatry and mental health diagnoses in detail and there are few reliable resources on which they can draw. This comprehensive guide to psychiatry and the mental health system, written by a psychiatrist and counsellor, aims to fill that gap.

The book is intended for counsellors and psychotherapists but will be helpful to others in the mental health field. It explains the organisation and delivery of mental health services in the UK, the theories and concepts underpinning the practice of psychiatry, the medical model of psychiatric diagnosis and treatment, the main forms of mental disorder, how to work therapeutically with people with a diagnosed mental disorder and how to work with risk of suicide and self-harm. The text is designed to support continuing professional development and training and includes activities, points for learning/discussion and comprehensive references.

**Available at discounted price with free UK postage from
www.pccs-books.co.uk**